# THE CHALLENGE
# OF AUTOMATION

## Papers Delivered at the National
## Conference on Automation

| | |
|---|---|
| JOSEPH C. O'MAHONEY | WALTER BUCKINGHAM |
| DONALD P. CAMPBELL | JOHN DIEBOLD |
| WALTER P. REUTHER | JOSEPH A. BEIRNE |
| JAMES B. CAREY | ADAM ABRUZZI |
| JACK CONWAY | I. W. ABEL |
| NAT GOLDFINGER | |

Public Affairs Press, Washington, D. C.

# EXPLANATORY NOTE

Convened under the auspices of the Committee on Economic Policy of the Congress of Industrial Organizations, the National Conference on Automation was held in Washington, D. C., on April 14, 1955. The major papers delivered at this conference are presented in the first four chapters of the present publication. Supplementary comments are included in the fifth chapter.

The members of the CIO Committee on Economic Policy are Emil Rieve (chairman), Joseph A. Beirne, L. S. Buckmaster, James B. Carey, David J. McDonald, Jacob S. Potofsky, Walter P. Reuther, and Stanley H. Ruttenberg (director).

# THE CHALLENGE
# OF AUTOMATION

# CONTENTS

# PUBLIC POLICY IMPLICATIONS

## By Senator Joseph C. O'Mahoney

New problems are not created by new words. The problems appear first and the words afterward, but occasionally new words are invented to make old problems seem new. Such is the case with the new multisyllabic word "automation." It is not to be found in the latest dictionary, to be sure, yet it represents a problem which came into existence with the first machine tool or even the first wheel.

Those who feared and sought to wreck the first machines because they conceived them to be destroyers of jobs were unable to see that every new machine can create a new demand by making possible the production of cheaper and more numerous commodities. Even though every new machine displaced some workers, nevertheless by reason of the fact that the new machines generally meant more goods at lower prices, their introduction in the end created more jobs and raised the standard of living. This result was achieved, however, in the main without regard to the hardships visited upon the displaced worker and in some cases even a displaced community. As inventions became more complex and more productive, they did in fact destroy the jobs of the men displaced by the new machine. Frequently this displacement came at a time when the displaced worker was no longer able to find a job for which he was trained, so that he and his family dropped in the social and economic scale. Industrial progress, therefore, was marked by a trail of hardship and distress for individuals, and also for communities no longer capable of being supported by displaced industries.

Automation signifies the most recent development of the age of mechanization. It appears now, however, upon a larger stage because it is an instrument of national business. It is used by the huge corporate units which employ thousands of workers and sometimes have plants in scores of cities scattered throughout the country

1

without respect to State lines. The entire population of the United States now has the opportunity to see clearly that the push-button, industrial system has such widespread effects upon our whole social, economic, and political structure that a Congressional study is unavoidable. In the first place, the investment required to build and to install the new automatic devices is beyond the ability of local communities or local banks to produce. It is a production method which can exist only with mass production and mass markets. It is therefore a problem which is beyond the political jurisdiction of local communities or even States to regulate in the public interest. If it is not regulated, it must of necessity make its own rules and those rules will be concerned with investment profit and loss rather than with the effects upon the worker and the local community.

The object of such a study would be the adoption of such rules of public policy as to make certain that automation would be a stabilizing and not a disturbing element in the national economy.

The modern world has been at the brink of the abyss of nuclear war, a danger which can be avoided only if we have the sense to realize that moral, social, and economic progress for all constitutes the only safeguard of our cherished liberties and freedom. It is against this threatening background that we must consider the meaning and the possibilities of automation. What contribution can it make to winning this struggle for the survival of man? What problems may it raise which might even momentarily impair our strength for the cold war?

Thus viewed, we are forced to concede at the outset that any improved devices or techniques, be they electronic, mechanical, or simply human "know-how," which will add to the productive effectiveness of our resources, must be welcomed and recognized as desirable. That was perhaps easier to see during the recent world war when manpower was scarce and it was necessary to resort to more mechanization to increase production. A plant which was as efficient as many had hoped the ordnance plant at Rockford would be, would have then been readily acceptable without fear or question. If a factory, no matter how automatic, could save manpower for other jobs in the military effort, so much the better.

Why, then, are we concerned about automation today, even to the extent of holding such enlightening conferences as this one in which we are participating? The process of obtaining the maximum product with the least effort—the best use of our human and physical resources—is a goal for which we must strive just as vigorously under the conditions of the cold war as we had to do during the hot war, and as we must now do during the more active phases of the ideological struggle which our generation faces. It is certainly clear on the side of production that good public policy must accept the fruits of automation and encourage its progress to the extent that they improve living conditions for a constantly expanding circle of people.

It is clear that good government really exists to promote human welfare and that its paramount interest and duty lie in promoting the well-being of those who live under its shelter. Good public policy must, therefore, make certain that the human costs of material progress are kept at a minimum. If automation is to turn workers out on the streets, forcing them to compete with each other in a bitter struggle for ever fewer and fewer jobs, public policy dare not ignore it. Mass unemployment and economic depression would be almost as damaging to the foundations of our free society as the threat from without. So we are necessarily talking about Federal policy.

Fortunately, in this respect the Congress of the United States has already taken a long step forward under the Employment Act of 1946. Under that Act, the Federal Government has obligated itself to use its resources to create the conditions making for maximum employment—that is, to foster and promote conditions which will afford job opportunities for all those who are desirous and capable of working.

The greatest obstacle to the advancement of automation and the realization of its productive fruits lies in the possibility that the economy would fail to find other useful work for those who might be displaced by it. The whole process of increased production at one point would be defeated if human resources are wasted elsewhere. Both from the standpoint of needing the increased product and from the standpoint of performing its proper role in respect to its people, government must see that individual human beings are not made to suffer because of our vaunted technological progress. Public policy must consequently beware of and anticipate the temporary and long-run problems which may arise from such developments. Simply because we recognize and discuss these problems is, of course, no reason for fear.

During the time when the Temporary National Economic Committee was studying the structure and trends in American industry, we devoted considerable time to this problem of impact and significance of technological development upon the country. At that time we had to consider these developments against the backdrop of sizeable unemployment. Happily, that is less true today, so that if we plan ahead we can do so calmly and rationally.

It seems to me appropriate, therefore, that we again look at these trends and development in the light of the newly accepted responsibilities of Government in helping to insure adequate job opportunities.

Since the Joint Committee on the Economic Report is charged with the responsibility of making continuing studies of matters relating to employment, stability, and growth, that Committee tentatively plans to probe deeper into the subject matter behind the title of this paper—i. e., public policy implications of automation. The subcommittee considering this study has, of course, not fully formulated its plans. I cannot, therefore, say precisely what the subcommittee will do or what other members may have in mind in this respect.

Speaking, thus, for myself, I hope and expect that we will try to find out how automation may be made to pay its way in terms of human welfare. More specifically, we are concerned with how should public policy be adjusted to deal with such things as: (1) the possible and probable displacement of personnel; (2) the possible shifts and distortions which may arise in the distribution of mass purchasing power; (3) the sound and equitable distribution of the expected gains in productivity; (4) the impact of automation upon our business structure. There are doubtless a number of other questions which may come to mind as we go on—for example, the effect of automation upon the volume and regularity of private investment. But let us look a little more specifically upon the special problem areas thus suggested.

Since Government and public policy deals with human beings, public policy is particularly concerned with the displacement of personnel. One must be concerned about this as a short-run problem, even though one has confidence that the necessary adjustments can and will be made in the longer run. Whether or not a given bit of technological advancement actually creates as many jobs as it wipes out, no one can know. In the long run, the answer is "Yes." In the short run, it is too often "No." We do know that in the past we have in this country witnessed startling new technological advances which in the end have reduced costs and added to the demand for goods and services, so that more and more people have been employed. Introduction of the dial telephone has brought with it expanded use and resulting investment and expanded payrolls. The delivery of ready-mixed concrete has certainly made for more construction and hence more jobs in the construction industry than we might ever have hoped for under old methods of the gravel sieve, the shovel, and the cement-mixer's hoe. The fact that we have adjusted to wave after wave of technological advance in the past is too obvious to need extensive demonstration. The resultant capacity of American industry to produce an ever increasing volume of goods and services out of its manpower and machines has been a striking characteristic of our economic development. It is important that we preserve the conditions which have given us this self-generating force for economic good in the past. The fact that we have been able heretofore to adjust to technological progress is no guarantee that we shall be able to adjust as successfully to automation. This arises from the fact that automation necessarily is a change which will affect the whole country in a comparatively brief time, while most technological changes in the past were gradual.

The feeling of satisfaction over past gain does not, of course, belittle the hardships by way of loss of income suffered by displaced workers themselves while looking for and adjusting themselves to a new job. It does not belittle the individual tragedies which come when a man's hard-earned skills are suddenly made obsolete by introduction of new robots and techniques. Rather, it is a warning that a policy of drift would be dangerous in the face of automation.

We have, it is true, built into our economic and political system today a program for unemployment benefits. These should serve as a partial cushion for sudden displacements. Unemployment compensation is, however, almost of necessity a short-term palliative. We ought to know how much faith we can put in it in the face of automation. We certainly cannot depend upon it to the extent of dismissing the questions of proper public policy toward jobless workers, no matter how temporary their displacement may turn out to be.

The subcommittee of which I have spoken should, I believe, give consideration to just what the Government can and should do in the way of assisting and retraining those displaced or likely to be displaced. It seems to me that the first cost of retraining should, as they say, "fall upon the industry." It should not be allowed to fall upon Government, making it necessary for Government to "make work" by public expenditures on what was called "boondoggling" during the recovery movement in the early 30's. The principle upon which all policy should be based, it seems to me, is the recognition of what the founders of the Constitution had in mind when they established this Nation. They were thinking of people, they were thinking of justice, they were thinking of tranquillity, they were thinking of welfare, they were thinking of permanent liberty—and all these objectives, so clearly set forth in the Preamble to the Constitution, were meant for the enjoyment of the living man.

Every technological improvement in our age which necessarily affects the national social, economic, and political system must be weighed by the humanitarian standards of the Constitution. It should be able to pay its own way, not merely in terms of the obsolescence of existing plant and machinery, but in the more fundamental sense, giving due recognition to the human costs by way of severance pay and retraining and improving worker skills.

Automation, like other technological developments, usually calls for an up-grading of jobs. It increases the opportunity for talent but at the same time greatly increases the need for specialized training. This is particularly true of the maintenance and operation of highly technical electrical and electronic equipment. Since standards of education are generally considered a public responsibility, social responsibility will mean that the Government must adopt policies which will assure old as well as new workers the opportunity to secure needed retraining. If public policy allows private employers to shirk this responsibility, it will have to be accepted as a public responsibility in any case.

Another question to which I believe Congressional consideration should be given involves the possible distortions which may arise in the distribution of purchasing power resulting from the substitution of automatic devices for human labor. Automation must never be permitted to make an automaton of the man. If it should result merely in the production of more products with fewer persons receiving the purchasing power with which to take the increased supply off the market, it would defeat itself. Automation will succeed only if it continues to increase demand for the enlarged supply of commodities it makes, and at the same time creates an ever-expanding purchasing power among the masses to make the necessary market. This market can be created, where automation is used, both by more leisure and more salary for the workers.

We know that consumers have urgent and expanding needs. We know that these needs are translated into actual, effective demand, however, only when consumer purchasing power keeps pace with the ability to produce. While it is obviously true that the automatic factory will be a great user of materials and manpower, we ought not to forget, as Mr. Reuther has pointed out, that the automatic machines do not shop around at the department stores or durable goods stores to buy and consume their own output. During the depression years, there was a recognizable absence of a widespread distribution of purchasing power. Since that time we have, as a product of considered public policy by fiscal and other means, brought about some reduction in the disparity of incomes. The introduction of automation must not be allowed to wipe out the progress we have made in creating the mass markets so indispensable to the success of the system of mass production. The collective capital which the modern giant corporation invests in automation must be persuaded to recognize that higher skills and better training should be required of the supervisors who run these machines, and therefore that trainings for the social and economic responsibilities of automation are a proper cost of this technological progress.

It has been pointed out that the technology of automation is likely to find its fullest use in the so-called "administered price" industries where prices are notoriously insensitive to decreases in cost. Serious problems of public policy will thus arise if the cost savings in the costs of production are not passed through by way of the consumer price reductions needed to absorb the enlarged volume of production. We must anticipate this problem. We must not wait until unsold goods pile up on the shelves and we are in the midst of an inventory recession. If we neglect it till then, Government will nonetheless be expected to counter by turning to the traditional anti-depression tools at its service—monetary, fiscal, and public works expenditures, for example. It is not a question of public policy or no public policy, but what public policy, foresighted or belated.

This leads us directly into the next question—how should the gains of automation and its increased production be distributed among workers, consumers, and investors? What can public policy do to help diffuse the gains throughout the economy as a whole? What, if anything, should public policy do so that they do not constitute permanent windfalls for those who happen to be sitting in the front row when the changes occur?

The immediate suggestion is the recognition of the fact that automation is a development which, unless it is properly regulated under existing authority of the Constitution, could easily become stronger than government itself. The American system of government was designed to guarantee that people, and not any group, or class, or individual, should be the source of the authority to which the people must bow. The modern world is face to face with the challenge of collectivism. Communistic collectivism and fascist collectivism are philosophies through which a self-chosen dictator or group of dictators control the government and tell the people what they may and what they must do. The democratic-republican system of government, upon the other hand, is one in which the people prescribe the powers of the government and tell their public officials what they may do. Under our system, trade and commerce are just as much under the authority of the people as are the courts, the Executive, and the Congress. When, however, collective industry, trade, and commerce can use automation according to the desires or the will of the private managers, without responsibility to public authority, then the American political system will be undergoing a revolution.

It behooves both capital and labor to understand this basic characteristic of our government. Certainly the owners of capital as a group must understand that automation may be successfully used only if it is used to create markets, not only by increasing demand but by multiplying purchasing power. And labor as a group could face the threat of unemployment with greater equanimity if there were assurances under public authority that the worker would receive his just share in the division of the increased product and wealth resulting from automation.

Mr. Walter Reuther took a statesmanlike position when he recognized the desirability of technological progress, saying: "We will never question whether we want a big or little pie of national wealth to divide or deviate from our conviction that the big pie is always the easiest to split."

One way, of course, in which gains may be absorbed would be in a generally reduced work week. If we can get machines to do work heretofore done by men, we might look forward to a further shortening of the average work week. Within the lifetime of men now working, average hours have been reduced from 50 per week to just less than 40. Perhaps automation and the electronic age will do even more.

In connection with the possibility of increased leisure time, one can, of course, find some hope that the burdens of displacement will be eased by an expansion of employment and investment in the industries serving our leisure-time activities. If the time should come when the three-day week end became a reality, we can be sure that there will have to be substantial investment and large numbers of new jobs created in private recreational facilities as well as the public facilities—highways, parks, etc.

The Government and the public likewise have a great stake in the impact of automation upon the business structure. Just what that impact will be is a matter for investigation and study. On the one hand, the movement is likely to call for expensive plant installations. Instead of an assembly line made up of a series of small, more or less standard machines, these will all be tied together into a mammoth, special-purpose, complicated machine. The result, it would appear, is almost certain to give added advantage to the large enterprises in the mass production industries. To the extent that the movement contributes to a further concentration of economic power, the necessity for large government to deal with these concentrations will be increased.

The advance of technology and of science in decade after decade has been ways and means of recovering from the junk-heap of old industries new values for the production of new commodities and new wealth. It is difficult to recover any but moral values from the human junk-heaps created by unemployment and economic mismanagement. If we recognize, as we must, that this Government of the people, then we must recognize that the power granted to Congress in the Constitution to regulate commerce was a power intended to provide for the protection of people. This protection must be measured not in terms of the coming generation alone but in terms of the present generation and the generation that is passing. I have no doubt whatsoever that the American system of Government, set up in the American Constitution, is sufficient to provide the rules and regulations under which industry, trade, and commerce under automation can be so regulated as to be beneficial for our entire society.

Men do not live by jobs alone and the kind of a country in which we will live is dependent upon the spiritual and cultural values which we foster.

If the automatic factory and the push-button civilization bring only a small part of the product, leisure, and labor saving that some students predict, we shall have to think seriously about the over-all problem which Adolf Berle suggested in his *Saturday Review* article on the democratic future. Mr. Berle observed: "For the first time in recorded history a huge population is concerned with the problem, not merely of living, but of what life they want to live. The 'good life' of the Greek idealists will be within reach if we know what to choose." Perhaps it isn't too much a matter for democratic government to help in influencing the kinds of choices made by its citizens. But it certainly is an important matter for public policy to see that levels of education, understanding, and appreciation are raised so that the new materialistic processes shall not crush our basic moral forces but, rather, under the spiritual concepts which guided the founders of our Government, make for a better world as well as a richer and easier one.

# APPLICATIONS AND USES

BY JOHN DIEBOLD

*Editorial Director, "Automatic Control"*

Two hundred years ago, our Western World experienced the beginnings of a movement that changed the lives of all mankind. It took men off the fields and out of small shops and put them, for the first time, into factory life.   Hence, it gave us mass production, and through mass production the first civilization in history in which luxury was not confined to a few.

It gave us as well a sense of hurry, of time, which is still unknown in countries that are pre-industrial.   It changed agricultural societies into mighty industrial nations.   It altered the face of our own country; and it produced wealth, the like of which the world had never before seen.

We were taught in school to call this movement the "Industrial Revolution."   But, now, we find that name being changed. We call it today, the *First* Industrial Revolution.   For, suddenly, it seems that our whole nation is aware of a new movement—a new force—which holds promise of great social change and increased economic benefit for us all.   We are told that a new Industrial Revolution is in the making, in fact that it has already begun.   This *Second* Industrial Revolution is called by the name *automation*.

I think that there is a good deal more confusion surrounding the word automation than some of us would like to admit.   Perhaps, the confusion begins in another word—in the much overused word, *revolution*.   There seems to be a political revolution somewhere in the world at least once a year.   And every time a manufacturer puts a new girdle on the market, he calls it revolutionary, too.   I even saw a sign in a New York bakery recently that read:   "Revolutionary New Old Fashioned Doughnuts!"

But when we use the word "revolution," to describe the new movement of automation, we obviously do not mean it in the sense

12

of political upheaval or of something that is merely new, gadgety or startling. We mean it in the broadest sense—in the sense in which we speak of the Industrial Revolution.

When we look back on that great upheaval two centuries ago, what was it that gave to it the name Industrial *Revolution*? Was it just the wonderful machines that lightened man's toil? No, I think it was much more than this.

Nor was the word "revolution" adopted because of the riots that accompanied the introduction of some of these machines. Nor was it intended to describe the speed with which these changes took place.

The Industrial Revolution was *revolutionary* in the broadest possible sense of the word. It created a whole new environment for mankind—a whole new way of life. What it gave to history was much more than the steam engine and the cotton gin, the railway and the power loom. It gave society a whole new tempo, a whole new way of life.

If we are going to apply the word, "revolution," to the changes that are taking place today, we must be very careful how close we draw the analogy or we are likely to find that we have created more confusion than understanding.

As for the word "automation" I quite frankly find it very difficult to define. This may sound strange coming from someone who has had a good deal to do with its widespread use. But automation has come to mean so many things to so many people that I suspect it is losing its usefulness. To some automation seems nothing more than mechanization. It is a label that is applied to anything automatic, or even semi-automatic. To others it conveys a sense of robots; of machines that think and will eventually take over all of man's functions. To still others it connotes that panacea for all our troubles culminating in the seven day week-end.

Norbert Wiener calls automation a "barbarous" word. After going through several anguished hours trying to write a useful definition for presentation this morning I am inclined to agree with him, though for rather different reasons.

My most usual way of avoiding the dilemma of definition is to explain that automation has two quite distinct meanings. On the one hand, we have what I like to call "Detroit Automation," or advanced mechanization. On the other, we have the growing use of automatic feedback control. Intelligently pursued, both avenues of development can lead to highly automatic operation. Both approaches are technologically and economically significant, and both are certainly worthy of much consideration and analysis.

The areas of application of Detroit automation are quite clear. It is a form of automation already familiar to most of you. It is generally limited to long runs of identical product. To some extent the length of run requirement can be mitigated by clever design of both machine and workpiece but Detroit automation is fundamentally a long run production method.

It is a natural outgrowth of both the production line and the machine tool. The essential characteristic of Detroit automation is the *integration of machines with one another.* This is a very important point and it is one to which I will return.

In the Cleveland and Buffalo plants of the Ford Motor Company electric and hydraulic controls permit the loading and unloading of special purpose multistage machine tools, while large transfer machines provide for automatic movement of workpieces from one operation to the next. During the past few years this type of automation—whose development can be traced through at least one hundred and fifty years of evolution—has become common in the automotive industry, and has spread to other areas of the metal working, electrical and electronic, meat packing and food processing industries. Wherever repetitive operations are to be performed, over long runs of product Detroit automation stands a good chance of application.

The key quality of the second kind of automation—feedback— is *self-regulation.* While the First Industrial Revolution provided machines that lightened man's toil, it is the technology of feedback in Today's Industrial Revolution that is providing machines that perform the functions of control.

Here we have a whole new technology which permits the automatic manufacture of *short* as well as long runs of varying product. This second type of automation thus breaks through the limits of mechanization and extends the benefits of automatic production to the job shop. Since by far the largest proportion of this country's production is in the form of job shop runs the ability to produce these short runs automatically is a very important accomplishment.

But the application of feedback is even broader than is implied by this fact alone. The essence of feedback is the handling and control of information. Since this information may refer to tool movement on a lathe; or a liquid flowing through a pipe; or a file in an insurance office, the application of this kind of automation is very wide. So far feedback has been used most extensively in the process industries but it is now being introduced to metal working and through the medium of the electronic computer into the office as well.

Thus far I have avoided putting myself out on a limb by actually defining automation. But it seems to me that after distinguishing these two developments, Detroit automation and feedback, it is possible to distill from them a common and unique quality—the integration of machines with each other into fully automatic, and, in some cases, self-regulating systems. In this sense automation is something of a conceptual "break-through." It is an attitude of mind, and a production objective as much as it is a technology. Its roots can be traced far back in our industrial history, and it makes use of old, as well as new techniques—but it is in itself an essentially new way of approaching industrial problems. It will affect every kind of industry, not only manufacturing and processing, but retailing, transportation, communication, and commerce as well. It is as accessible to the small business man as to the giant corporation.

I would like to dwell briefly on the last point, for it is fundamental to understanding how wide is the area of application of automation. Perhaps the least talked about but most significant aspect of the technology of feedback is *flexibility*. For example, by using the principle of feedback in machine tool control we obtain the flexibility necessary to machine pieces by varying specifications automatically yet economically. Conventional automatic machine tools are controlled by mechanical devices, such as cams or levers. They cannot change from one product specification to another without costly and extensive adjustments and can, therefore, machine automatically only long runs of identical products.

In a consumer economy as dynamic as ours, the shop that is wedded to one product, because of heavy machine investment, soon finds himself in an untenable position. Special purpose automatic machines enable him to produce at low cost but they are incapable of producing a variety of products and rust long before they are paid for, except when used in those industries having substantially stable demand for their products. The small manufacturer is most severely limited by the high capital requirements of conventional automatic equipment.

It is this very situation that feedback automation now promises to alter. Through *flexible,* automatic control, machines can be made more versatile as well as automatic. *No longer must the benefits of automatic production be limited to large operations.* Now, the job and semi-production shop—which as I have said account for the largest volume of our national production—can enjoy the fruits of automation.

I have mentioned the word "revolution" often during this paper. There can be little doubt that automation deserves the title. But it is just as true, that this, our Second Industrial Revolution, differs as much from the first, and in as many respects, as it is similar to it. Each has its own characteristics, and in the future, when historians examine the record, they are more apt to be surprised by the differences than the similarities.

The first, the foremost, and the most startling of these differences, lies in the fact that automation has created new jobs before its machines have replaced many old jobs. We are all aware that technological progress always produces these results. What we worry about is a time lag during which men have no work between the old and the new jobs. That is what happened, in part, during the First Industrial Revolution. This time a new pattern seems to be developing.

Automation has already produced a new industry in America. There are more than 1000 companies engaged wholly or partly in the manufacture of automation equipment. Their aggregate output last year totaled more than 3 billion dollars.    And, they are one of the fastest growing industries in America.

In all our thinking on this subject, it seems to me, we concentrate too much on what automation will do to our *present* way of doing things and we do not give enough thought to the things automation will enable us to do for the first time.    Automation has opened up a whole new world to us.    Feedback controls have made it possible to reach entirely new levels of achievement.

For example, we would not have atomic energy if it were not for feedback control.    No man could operate valves or hand controls deep within the dreadful flux of the atomic reactor.    Here, remote feedback devices must perform our work.    Without servo motors and other feedback equipment, it would be impossible for us to operate our atomic plants.

Nor would the manufacture of polyethelene be possible without the use of feedback control.    This common plastic used to package many products you use every day requires exquisite operational precision in reacting time, temperature and pressures.    Without automatic control of this process, the product would turn out to be only a useless wax.

Automation can make economical many products which it is currently impossible to produce.    The chemical companies, such as the petroleum companies, would not be able to control many of their split-second reactions, and we would be without many new products were it not for feedback control.    A whole line of precision products—which would be hopelessly costly if manufactured with human supervision—suddenly became worthwhile under automatic supervision.

Too often, we speak of automation and the speed with which it is being incorporated into our economy, we find ourselves hoping that this will be a slow transition—a gradual integration.    This is likely to be the case, but, in actuality, I suspect we ought to be thinking in terms of speeding it up rather than slowing it down.

There are many reasons to adopt this avenue of thought, but the most compelling reason is the present divided state of the world. One does not need to be a mathematician to understand how greatly the free people of the world are outnumbered by the totalitarians.

We must in some manner make up for this difference in manpower. Automation offers one possibility. If this, alone, were the only justification for automation, it would, in my opinion, be sufficient.

A less urgent, most compelling reason, is the simple fact that we Americans have grown to expect a steady and substantial increase in our standard of living. We hope, and we expect that, as time goes by, we shall have to devote smaller and smaller proportions of our day to the trying task of earning a living. Being realists, we understand that this increase in productivity is not God-given and can only be brought about by producing more and more goods with a lessened and more rational and dignifying human effort.

The startling fact is that while our population grows in leaps and bounds, the working force of the nation is currently growing smaller in relation to the total. The age of retirement is decreasing while the average age at which young people enter the work force is increasing. Moreover, the generation now coming of working age was born during the great depression and is smaller by far than the group below working age. Thus, the pressure on the job market will be lessening during the next decade—the period when the great changes of automation will be made.

If we are to improve our standard of living—indeed, if we are to hold what we have—we shall need more machines and better machines. In short, we will not only be able to tolerate automation, we will need it.

It would, of course, be foolish for me to contend that automation is not without its growing pains. For any of us to minimize the widespread social and economic effects that automation is sure to bring would be to close our eyes to a fact that is already part of everyday life. But I would like to emphasize that no one, today, is in a position to do more than speculate on the nature and extent of these social and economic effects, for no one has yet made the detailed analysis that is necessary for their true understanding.

While it is obvious that in the long run, automation will be of tremendous benefit to us all, it is the short run that worries most of us. Despite the fact that in today's Industrial Revolution, the new jobs are being created before the old ones are destroyed and that the pressure will be on us to simply hold our own with a smaller percentage of our population in the workforce, there still exists the danger that temporary dislocations of personnel will occur in some cases. We should begin planning for this now.

I do not intend to masquerade as an expert on the labor effects of Automation. But there are certain things which are obvious to all thinking men, and I would like to mention them briefly.

Fundamental to the successful integration of Automation into our mechanized society is the recognition by all parties concerned— unions, management, and government—that they have a common interest. No one, least of all, the American businessman, wants to see increased unemployment. All of us stand to gain by Automation as long as we stand together.

Education is our primary need. The public must be helped to learn the true meaning of Automation—not in the alarmist terms which describe it as the replacement of workers by machines, but in its true meaning—the production of more wealth with less human effort. We must recognize that this is something good, and we must learn to use it.

From the long range point of view, it is probable that automation will be responsible for a new type of labor force. In our dynamic economy with its ever-increasing needs there is no set number of jobs, but rather, a constant shifting of *kinds* of jobs. The implication of such a shift for retraining of workers is an important challenge facing both organized labor and management.

Men whose specific jobs may someday be replaced by machines should be stimulated to begin their training in the newer skills which Automation creates. Automatic factories will *not* be workless factories. There will be the need for more and more technicians and highly skilled maintenance men. We are already woefully short of personnel in this regard. The statisticians say that we need some 25,000 more engineers and 75,000 more technicians each year than we are now training. Russia, I've been told, is training some four times the number that we do and this ratio will be even more distressing in the years ahead unless we do something about it. We need to begin now to narrow this gap between our technical requirements and manpower.

It strikes me that much of the concern over adverse labor effects of automation is due to what I call "obituary accounting"—that is, toting up the number of workers replaced by a machine, multiplying that sum by the number of machines, and tagging the end results "unemployment." This practice assumes that only a set number of jobs exist in our economy and ignores the fundamental fact that *our needs increase continually*. To ignore this fact is to sell short the marvelous capacity for growth and production that has been at the heart of American industrial expansion.

Automation holds no threat to our economy. By giving us enormously increased productivity, on the contrary, it promises to invigorate the economy. I think it fair to say that automation offers as great a challenge, and reward, as any which we have ever known.

# TECHNOLOGICAL CONSIDERATIONS

By DONALD P. CAMPBELL

*Massachusetts Institute of Technology*

The principal activity of man is to make a living. There are two ways to do this: produce a commodity; render a service. Basically, production is the handling of materials. Service is the handling of information. Production involves the taking of raw material and converting it to a product. Parts are assembled into mechanisms. Several products placed together can be made into new materials. Service is processing action taken upon paper work (loosely speaking) to bring about office record-keeping, sales, inventory control, purchasing and marketing. The major activity of man is found in these two basic processes: *materials handling* and *information handling*. How rapidly and effectively he can move material and interpret information becomes a measure of his economic progress. It determines whether he can earn a living and also have energy and leisure for personal development.

I believe that technology has made a great contribution to both labor and management by demonstrating that mathematical foundations exist which are capable of explaining how materials can be processed and information used and stored. These mathematical ideas are not yet so well established as are the theories of chemistry and physics, but they will be. It is only a matter of time. The mathematical concepts now being tested will yield a theory of the production process and a theory of the service process. Combined, they will provide a theory of the business process.

Individual automatic machines, automatic factories, and automatic offices are *not* the most important issue. Any sequence of mechanical manipulations that a man can make with his hands and feet, however simple or complex, can be made by a machine, provided there is no "value judgment" required. A robot can play the violin, if we do not insist that music be produced. Computing machines can perform all the mental gymnastics of arithmetic,

21

algebra, and the solving of equations that man struggles with.    They can reduce to rote the intricate procedures that he cannot even re-member.    This does not mean, however, that a computing machine thinks.    The robots and the computers, the automatic factories and the automatic offices are only replacing the hand tools that served man a century ago, and the simple power tools and desk calculations that have served him recently.    In my opinion, there is no limit to the productive capacity that can be reached by the individual and no limit to the flow of information that can pass through his hands, if he is given the proper tools and taught how to use them.

Much discussion about automation—its benefits and its evils—seems to be based upon emotion rather than fact.    When time is of the essence in high speed operations, and we know the limitations upon how fast muscles can move, there is no point in expecting a man to do things that his hands and fingers cannot possibly do.    When the amount of data and information that he must procure to reach a decision exceeds the capacities of his senses—that is, his eyes, his ears, and his sense of touch—then instrumentation and computational aid must be provided for him.    We do not eliminate him by a robot or a computer.    We give him the automatic machine or conputer to enchance and magnify his skills.    Robots, automatic machines, and computers must be, and can be designed so that the worker understands what they can do and can make them perform for him.

The issue which I believe has the far greater import is the fact that our future production and service operations can be so conceived that they combine men and machines in balanced proportion—con-ceived with a knowledge of man's physical skills and his ability to manipulate and supervise machines.    The machines can be designed to be the servant of man and to respond readily to his skills.    He can be given the role of monitor where value judgment *does* count.    When labor and management combine their effort to exploit these two ingredients—the automatic machine and the computer—, when they use the knowledge of the limitations of human physical and mental processes, and when the new concepts of mathematics put at their disposal by the modern technologist are properly used, new plants and complicated new processes can be made that may project this country into a golden age of production and service.

The processes which man uses have developed gradually. Changes have been evolutionary rather than revolutionary. Continuous improvement of the processes and continuous experimentation in how to join them to form complex manufacturing and service systems represent the growth pattern.

Increase in the size of our business operations has also been evolutionary. At first, processing operations involved only a single step or relatively few steps. Today we have entire sequences or systems of operations which consist of the procuring of raw material, the manufacture of goods, and their distribution and sale.

Production is basically a materials-handling operation. In agriculture, we produce food. The food is cleaned, cooked, or refrigerated to preserve its value. It is then distributed to a variety of storage centers where we draw upon it the year round. Pumping stations send natural gas through pipe-lines to residential and industrial regions. Textile fibers are made from chemicals and glass. They are formed and woven into cloth. Paper products are formed, printed upon, and distributed for use in our daily work. A multitude of building materials—wood, glass, fibers, and ceramics—are manufactured. Our greatest industries produce metals. Ore is reduced to crude metal. The crude metal is formed, rolled, and made into a great variety of products. Steel, aluminum and other metals are used in our bridges and buildings, our automobiles, and our radios and TV sets.

Service is an information-handling process. News is gathered, broadcast, telecast, and stored for record. In department stores, customer requests for merchandise pass through procedures of recording, checking against inventory, procurement, packaging, mailing, or shipping. Customer orders for bulk goods, such as steel, glass, and plastic, generally call for a variety of shapes, sizes and quantities. The orders must be collected and compared with stock on hand. They are usually filled from current production. If not, special production schedules are planned to fill them.

In marketing, distributing, banking, insurance, and government, the information-handling processes are extensive and intricate. Furthermore, processes have a distinct tendency to become more complex. Greater amounts of information must be handled, and handled more rapidly.   The need for increased versatility in handling information is apparent.

Of course, the two basic processes merge.   Business is made up of combinations of operations.   Some handle material; some handle information; some handle both.   In fact, a measure—an informational state—can be associated with every quantity or quality that describes the goods we make or the work we do.   This last point is a very important one.   It is the basis for our being able to establish a mathematical theory which explains and describes the behavior of the production and service processes in terms of their materials-handling and information-handling capacity.

The new technology is no different from the old.   The ideas which germinated and came to fruition fifteen years ago as we defended ourselves against aggression, are now available as a constructive, peace-time dividend on our effort.   Technology results from proved scientific ideas—not speculation.   Technology puts into practice those scientific ideas which are sound.   In the production and service processes it must stand a severe test:   Innovations must be those which men can learn to use and be willing to use—innovations which make possible greater productivity per unit of effort, greater service per unit of effort, and better quality of production and service.   A large amount of proved knowledge exists about human operators, automatic control, communications, and computation.   We should test it.

During the last war we learned the benefit gained by penetrating quantitative analysis.   The quantitative method means to go into detail, to obtain numbers, to use measurements and accurate data for design.   This is in contrast to a qualitative approach, which merely uses ideas that may be correct but which are not supported by numerical evidence.   The quantitative approach gives answers; the qualitative approach only indicates that answers may exist.   The quantitative solution to a problem when it can be obtained, proves to be time-saving.   We can often get from it a measure of the maximum possible capability of a mechanism or system.   Quantitative solutions permit us to plan bolder designs with confidence.   They also focus our attention on the important issues.

Today, when every one wants to make everything automatic, a quantitative approach is needed.   We must make thorough studies in order to design a highly automatic process or plant. More is needed than the construction and assembly of equipment which works without machine tenders or with only a small group of tenders. "Automation" follows logically *after* rigorous investigation of the production and service operations has shown that they are worth making automatic. A factory, an office, or a service organization must be thought of in terms of what we want to make, and how we can make it. After we know what we want to make, and how we can make it, the sequence of operations can be unified, mechanized, and made automatic. The plants and service organizations being planned today are too large and too expensive to warrant guesswork. Too many automatic factories are being "imagineered." There is no need for guesswork in considering automatic factories or automatic offices. A quantitative approach to the problem will show when they are economical and when they are not.

We can look upon production and service operations as systems of individual operations joined according to a well-organized pattern. An organizational pattern lies behind every present-day production, service, and business operation. In fact, the same business operation can often be carried out successfully and competitively by more than one organizational plan.

The organizational pattern, the cause-and-effect relationship in materials handling and information handling, gives us the possibility of measuring production and service system performance. We can compare actual performance of an operation with its theoretically maximum possible performance. We can decide what portion of the system needs improvement in order to bring it up to par with the others. Or we can decide that the whole organizational plan is out of date and needs replacement.

It is the performance of the combination that counts. What good is an automatic factory without mechanized distribution and marketing? Why should automatic food dispensers in a modern industrial plant be hamstrung by old-fashioned cooking methods?

Processes never operate in a condition of equilibrium. They are continuously disturbed, and are continuously manipulated and corrected against these disturbances by either manual or automatic action. Their action is dynamic. The rapidity with which they recover from disturbances and the speed with which they can shift from one condition of action to another, measure how good they are. The speed of materials handling and the volume of information handling which indicate the productive capacity and the efficiency of our present-day operations are determined by their organizational pattern and their dynamic nature.

Dynamic systems can be unstable. They can get out of hand and oscillate. Much has been learned about the stability of dynamic systems in the last decade or two in the fields of servomechanism and military fire control. The causes of instability can be recognized. These are principally the momentary delays in the handling of information—the so-called "time lags" and the "noise" which "jams" our communication system. Instability can also result because of the improper manner in which one process is connected with another. There are procedures that tell us how to prevent oscillations from this cause.

The methods of mathematical analysis available not only make possible the study of the stability of large combinations of producing and serving organizations, but to some extent they indicate that the tightness with which we regulate the movement of materials and the handling of information in our complex modern industrial world may very well determine the dynamic stability of our whole economy. Regulation to prevent upsets and instability must itself be dynamic. For a tight dynamic system—and a tight system is necessary for productive strength—we must be ready to pay the price of some tendency toward instability. The ballerina who is *great* will be temperamental.

Automatic control is not something new. Processes have been controlled automatically since 1900—in fact, since the middle 1800's. And if one wanted to be very accurate, the ancient kings had automatic toys 2000 years ago. Some processes are quite easy to control. Others are difficult. Sometimes processes are so simple that a single man can do all the controlling that is necessary; others are so complicated that they require an entire working force of men and machines to manipulate them. In fact, there are many different varieties of control. Control may be manual without the aid of special machinery. It may nevertheless be automatic in the sense that a man continually monitors a process and makes it do what he wishes it to do. Automatic equipment may be in action, but may respond to a human supervisor. Then again, some processes may be fully automatic. Control always involves measurement, communication, decision, manipulation, and process response to both manipulation and disturbance.

When a man controls a process, he must be provided with information that tells him what is happening. He must be given a procedure pattern for manipulating the process and correcting it against upsets.

We have certainly studied much about "the human operator": that is, studies have been made to show how quickly the muscles can move in response to stimulation. We have also studied the amount of information that the eyes and ears can receive. For example, the instrument panel in the modern airplane is designed to increase and improve the ability of the pilot to gather information as he rapidly scans the panel preparatory to making a difficult maneuver. The automatic pilot or the controls are designed to match with his physical skills. Thus, to a certain extent, we can measure the ability of a man to receive information and his capacity for translating information into mechanical action.

When the requirement for control over any operation exceeds the dynamic response of the man, the automatic machine must be given to him as a tool.

Doubtless you have heard about "computer control." By this, people imply that the computing machines will run our plants and factories. In time, this could be so; but there is one important fact to note. A computer will do only what it is programmed to do. Its principal ability is to carry out complicated arithmetical and algebraic operations at high speed. It can do in a very short time calculations that take a man a long time to execute. Therefore, the computer will simply become an adjunct to the plant operator or supervisor. It will take data from measuring instruments, make calculations, and provide a group of answers from which the supervisor can choose.

The scientific theories which can guide us into an entirely new era of production and service capability as a nation are proved. We are already putting them into practice. However, I am inclined to feel that we are not putting them into practice quite rapidly enough. Every indication points to the need for more goods and more services in the immediate future.  Our population is growing, our demands for new things is growing.  If we are to keep our country in a strong position of defense our production and service industries must be as modern and up to date as they can possibly be.

It's possible we may not get increased productive and service capacity soon enough to meet our needs.  In spite of the new technology, there may be a limitation on our engineering capacity to produce.  Many of our plants and processes are so outmoded that automatic controls cannot be installed on them.  To engineer new plants and processes takes many, many hundreds, even thousands of engineering *man years* of work.

I see no rapid impact of automation on the working force of the United States.  In fact, I would urge labor to insist that it be given these modern "tools" as rapidly as possible so that old fashioned industries and outmoded operations can improve their competitive position.

Secondly, since the demand for automatic control will increase, we shall need components in great variety and number.  New mass-production industries will be needed for this production.  An important point to recognize is that automatic control equipment is precise equipment.  It is more difficult and more costly to make such equipment than it is to make much of our consumer goods.  Control and computer components are sometimes so tiny that they have to be made by special machines.

Thirdly, when we speed up production and increase information-handling capacity, it is very important not to have a plant shut down for more than a very short time.  Otherwise, material may pile up or information may exceed storage capacity.  Supervision of plant control will be a job that requires skill, quick thinking, and thoroughness.  Maintenance crews will have to work decisively and rapidly.  There will be no time for muddling through.  This calls for men especially trained in the modern ideas of how to maintain precise equipment.  It may be necessary to set up training programs or schools of "applied technology" to train the necessary working force in the maintenance of the new automatic machinery.

The last thought I should like to express is that the introduction of highly mechanized and automatic equipment in our plants and offices will give the people who are willing to accept them and use them greater productive capacity, better competitive position. The new technology is not confined to the United States. It is available for the whole world to use. Whether or not we use it, it is certain that somebody else will.

# INDUSTRIAL SIGNIFICANCE

By WALTER S. BUCKINGHAM, JR.
Associate Professor of Industrial Management
Georgia Institute of Technology

The word "automation" summarizes one of the most significant technological developments in history. To a Ford Motor Company vice president it is "a new concept, a philosophy, of manufacturing." To its disciples it promises as great an improvement over current methods of business operation as the mechanized factories of the Industrial Revolution proved over the guild craftsmen of the Middle Ages. Even to the sceptic automation offers the opportunity for greater output, shorter working hours, the creation of a host of skilled jobs in maintenance, design and engineering, safer working conditions and the production of new and better goods of standardized quality and with more efficient use of raw materials. However, the parallel between the development of this new technology and the Industrial Revolution of the eighteenth century has given rise to considerable speculation as to whether automation is likely to be accompanied by the same undesirable economic effects that accompanied the original industrialization process.

This paper proposes (1) to examine automation in the perspective of the long range growth of industrialization and the evolution of business organization; (2) to assess the speed and extent of automation in the future; (3) to analyze the economic problems which may arise with particular regard to industrial concentration, plant location, composition of the labor force and the level of employment.

If properly understood, applied, developed and controlled, automation, together with atomic energy, may provide the means for eliminating poverty for the first time in the history of the world. However, the economic implications must be carefully analyzed so that the mistakes of the first Industrial Revolution can be avoided and the benefits of this new technology more equitably distributed.

As a threat, automation is particularly serious because to oppose it would be to risk national defeat in the relentless technological race for productive supremacy in the world. For the most part, the leaders of the American labor movement have given evidence of their public responsibility by supporting technological innovations. There have been exceptions, to be sure, and they have been widely-publicized, but labor's record on this score is at least as good as that of management. Full employment and prosperity in recent years have taught both labor and management that there is more to be gained from progress than from restrictionism.

The concern of labor leaders over the possible consequences of automation has been widely misinterpreted as being a fear of science and invention. Hardly anyone is afraid of technological progress any more but this does not mean that all innovations must be accepted uncritically. Every advance of progress has brought with it serious economic and social problems. The steam engine laid the corner-stone of our prosperous, urban, industrial system with its high living standards and its boundless opportunities but it also destroyed the security, craftsmanship and spiritual peace which had existed in the rural, agricultural life of the Middle Ages. The modern industrial economy combines insecurity with its high living standards, specialization with its high output and anxieties and dangers with its limitless opportunities. Civilization itself brought with it a necessity of conforming to the will of organized groups. There is an old saying that you cannot bask in the morning sun of a new day without casting a shadow behind you.

Therefore, automation, like every other innovation which is in our tradition of technological progress, should be openly discussed so that its hidden dangers, if any, can be discovered, analyzed and properly controlled. The same spirit of inquisitiveness which produced automation and all other scientific achievements must be applied with equal rigor to the economic and social problems which automation, in turn, will produce. There have recently been suggestions from some people that it is akin to treason to investigate these problems, apparently on the theory that there would be no problems if only we would ignore them.

However, all of our historical experience testifies to the fact that an innovation of the scope of automation is bound to produce serious maladjustments in our economic and social structures. It is a fair bet that if there had been a political democracy in England in

1750 and if even a fraction of the hardships of the Industrial Revolution could have been foreseen, safeguards against them would have been developed and built into the economy so that the nineteenth century would not have witnessed the apalling misery and gross income equalities upon which our present high capital accumulation and living standards are based. It is an equally fair bet that the working people could have been secured against the great social costs of industrialization without any significant loss of incentives, technological progress or capital accumulation.

Regardless of whether automation turns out to be a second Industrial Revolution or merely an extension or acceleration of the mechanization process there is a possibility that its benefits may be largely dissipated by unemployment, hardships and human degradation unless it is properly understood and controlled. If, as some business leaders are claiming, there is nothing at all to worry about, then surely nothing will have been lost by an inquiry or even by the establishment of stand-by protective measures.

Automation means a continuous and integrated operation of a production system using electronic equipment to perform routine functions and regulate and coordinate the flow and quality of production. In its broadest usage it would include the operation of the productive and administrative processes of an industrial firm. Direct human labor would largely be eliminated from production, being retained mostly for systems analysis, programming, equipment maintenance and adjustment, and managerial decision making.

Automation is already being used in many industries as either a supplement or substitute for conventional assembly line operations. The more spectacular uses of automation, particularly in taking over administrative functions and in integrating them with productive processes, remain for the future. However, there can be no question about what the potential uses of automation are. It is merely a question of time, possibly five years or less, before electronic control of business operations becomes of age in the economy.

Those who understand both the principles of business procedure and electronic equipment are saying that computers will be able to use current sales forecasting analysis to automatically adjust and integrate the chain of interrelated operations such as management, planning, sales, supply, production, budgeting, and accounting.

Models, in the form of electrical networks, can be constructed and studied by economists. Artificial disturbances analogous to assumed changes in economic variables can be employed to determine the consequences of alternate courses of action. The enormous speed with which complicated problems can be solved greatly increases the possibility of experimentation within relevant time periods. For some business operations, computers can replace almost the entire workforce.

The immediate effects in the plant of the introduction of such a process are to substitute machinery for labor, set a continuous pace at which the plant must be operated, greatly increase production and provide a more comprehensive and efficient information gathering and handling system. The introduction of mass production methods at the beginning of the century had all of these effects and the result was a material alteration in the character of industry. It became necessary to develop an entirely new concept of the business organization.

The nineteenth century businessman fit the title economists gave to him—"entrepreneur." A strictly literal translation of this term is "undertaker" but the entrepreneur's function was to preside not at the burial but at the birth of a commercial venture. Specifically his functions were risk-taking and innovating. In the individualistic, frontier economy of the nineteenth century he was responsible to no one for his actions.

Mass production methods and the resulting growth of firms so large that they must depend on mass consumption for their continued existence changed all of this. Industrial and financial corporations grew so large that their risks could be pooled and losses accurately predicted and provided for. Self insurance arose as many firms outgrew even the insurance companies which had formerly assumed their risks. Even commercial risks declined as firms grew large enough to decentralize their operations and diversify their products.

The innovation function of the entrepreneur declined also. Innovations consist of inventions, improvements in techniques or in organization. Recently they have tended to become the product of large research laboratories rather than a flash from the brain of an ingenious inventor. As Alfred North Whitehead, the famous British philosopher once said, "The greatest invention of the nineteenth century was the invention of the art of inventing." Put some scientists in a well-equipped laboratory, pay them a fixed salary and they will invent or come up with new ideas at a predictable rate. Hence the almost constant annual increase in productivity of the last 60 years. Hence, also, the increasing obsolescence of the traditional functions of the entrepreneur.

In effect mass production technology led to a steady movement away from the authoritarianism of the Robber-Baron Era. That romantic despot largely vacated the American industrial scene being relegated now to a portion of the service and retail areas. This man of daring and imagination who relied on intuition and vision, or perhaps more accurately hunch supported by experience, became a technological casualty. The task of management changed. The shrewd bargain lost its significance. The top executive could no longer have knowledge of all the details of the firm's operations. Decisions began to be made by groups who put increasing reliance on the reports from the accounting sales, legal and other departments. The executive was forced to view his task as more than a mere manipulation of men and materials. He began to think of his functions as consisting of planning, coordinating, controlling the operations of the firm and harmonizing the interests of employees, investors, suppliers and customers.

Business ceased being an operation that could be stopped and started with small loss. Rather it became necessary that it be thought of as a flow of goods, sometimes requiring a twenty-four hour operation. The regulation of this flow became a dominant concern of the firm.

The function of the stockholder as a provider of risk capital has likewise declined. In the last ten years nearly two-thirds of all new, private capital has come from corporate profits plowed back into the business. Actually less than 5 % of new capital is really risk capital coming from common stock sales. Even common stock now often receives a fixed dividend much like the interest paid on loans. The vast increase in corporate size and the divorce of management from ownership has reduced stockholders' control of most large companies to virtually nothing. Thus it has not been the individual entrepreneur or the legal owner—the stockholder—who has emerged from the process of mechanization as the basic economic decision-maker, and the holder of economic power in the economy. It has been the corporate entity itself.

The large corporations today have much in common with a modern central government. In fact, some American corporations have a scope of operations which exceeds that of some of the smaller European countries. General Motors' annual gross revenue, for example, is greater than the national income of Yugoslavia. International and inter-firm contracts among these corporate giants partake the nature of treaties which cover an enormous field of operations. However, the gigantic size of modern corporations entails a public responsibility which cannot be avoided. Large firms can no longer shut down their operations, move their plants, invest in foreign countries or raise their prices without intimately affecting the lives of millions of people. They do not adjust their output and prices according to the economic conditions prevailing in the country. They create the economic conditions of the country by their price, wage and output policies.

Thus began the new concept of the business organization which, because of increasing interdependence of industry, has now become applicable to the entire economy. Just as the function of the businessman evolved from that of innovator and risk-taker to that of coordinator and controller of a high-speed, continuous process, so has the function of the government changed. A British statesman recently referred to the modern industrial economic system as being like a jet plane which cannot slow down without falling out of the sky. The interdependence of large corporations with each other, with the government and with all other sectors of the economy has become so complete that unemployment and other maladjustments can no longer be tolerated without seriously threatening the entire framework of our economic system. Hence large corporations have become, of necessity, semi-public institutions with responsibilities extending far beyond their balance sheets to the limits of the economy itself. Since they can consciously control the level of production and employment through their wage, price and output policies, they control the welfare of every citizen. In a democracy, then, it is clearly a responsibility of business and the government to insure a high and steady level of output and employment.

If the Industrial Revolution was the seed from which our economic system grew, then mass production was the flower and automation is the final fruit. This fruit must be eaten and enjoyed or it may rot and fall to the ground. Automation is the logical conclusion of the process of mechanization which is now over 200 years old. While the first Industrial Revolution was a new technology based on new forms and applications of power, automation is a new technology based on communications and control. Yet for the most part the consequences are the same. Furthermore while mechanization provided the economic basis for continuous, high-level production, automation adds a technical basis. Machines with instruments running them cannot economically be shut down. Thus automation carries to an extreme the presently known economic and social consequences of a mass production technology.

For the purpose of determining the extent to which automation can be applied to productive processes, industries can be divided into three groups. The first includes the various industries in which production can be reduced into a continuous flow process. Oil refining, flour milling, and chemical production are illustrations of industries in which automation has made, and should continue to make, significant progress. In other industries it is possible to revamp the productive mechanism in such a way as to convert it from a series of unit operations into a single endless process. While some industries utilize processes which are not conducive to automation, new methods of production may be conceived which are more acceptable.

A second class includes industries in which some automation is possible, but full or nearly complete automation is not likely. Indeed, it is possible that some industries may have automatic machines applied to seventy-five percent of their operations, yet the cost of making the plant completely automatic would more than offset the savings achieved from the use of partial application of automatic machines. In this category would be found industries which require substantial information-handling and accounting functions but in which the method of production or the nature of the product is not adaptable to continuous flow techniques. Such industries would include transportation, large-scale retailing, and the manufacture of certain nonstandardized consumer products like furniture.

The third group into which all industries may be classified includes those in which the highly individualistic nature of the product, the need for personal services, the advantages of small scale units or vast space requirements preclude any significant application of automatic controls. These would include agriculture, mining, professional fields, and most construction and retailing.

The very high initial expense of automatic control systems may prevent their installation by small firms. Although an enormous expansion is occurring in the manufacture of all kinds of electronic control devices, prices are not likely to be materially reduced for some time. The rapid rate of innovation in electronics and the continuous discovery of new applications of automatic control systems tend to postpone their mass production. Consequently these machines tend to be designed for individual order and therefore production must occur under the most expensive conditions. However, computer centers such as the one which we have established at Georgia Tech (which has two electronic computers, the E. R. A. 1101 and the C. R. C. 102 D) will soon make many services available to medium-sized firms on a part-time, rental basis.

Although a sizeable concentration of capital is necessary before a firm can achieve the economies of automatized operations, there is reason to believe that automatic control devices may lead to decentralization of plants. The growth of electric power transmission technology and the introduction of lightweight fabricating materials have already permitted plants to be located at great distance from power and supply sources. Since automatic equipment requires little direct labor, there will no longer be any compelling need to locate automatic production plants near large population centers. Of course, decentralization of production may be accompanied by further concentration of ownership if established firms take the lead in expanding into more remote areas. Decentralization of plants does not necessarily result in less concentration of market power. It may result in greater concentration.

Mechanization has also created capital surpluses which were partly employed in activity which led to further accumulation of wealth. Cumulative benefits have tended to accrue to those firms with excess capital. Automation, too, promises to reward the wealthier firms.

This is merely a continuation of the process which began with the Industrial Revolution 200 years ago and was accelerated by the introduction of mass production techniques about seventy years ago. However, unless there is a more vigorous anti-trust enforcement many firms may acquire more power than is necessary in order to achieve the economies of automation. Already there is a considerable concentration of power in a few large companies which can be justified only on the alleged economies of centralized financial control. For example, economies of production may require individual plants to be built on a large scale but can hardly be used to justify a holding company or chain control of a large number of similar units widely diversified geographically.

A second danger is that there may be abuses of such economic power as automation necessarily entails. Admittedly huge capital requirements and the need for established markets, a vast knowledge and experience and preferred banking, commercial and political connections already limit entry into many industries and give powerful advantages to the established firms. Much of this power is inherent in the scale of modern industrial operations and cannot be dispersed without a loss of efficiency. Automation promises to enhance this power and it will become increasingly important that a vigorous anti-trust policy prevent its misuse.

Automation does not promise to create as much secondary investment as have some of the earlier developments in technology. The introduction of the automobile and the resulting increase in primary investment in that industry stimulated a wave of investment in the oil, rubber, highway, and construction sectors of the economy. In this respect, automation probably will not make the far-reaching investment impression on the economy that the introduction and later improvements in automobiles, railroads, and canals, for example, created. Therefore, any loss of purchasing power due to a lower wage bill may not be offset by expenditures induced in other industries such as accompanied earlier advances in mechanization. Since the present industrial structure permits firms to reduce output and employment, rather than forcing them to reduce prices, when demand declines, it becomes necessary that fiscal policies not discriminate against lower income groups and that wages rise in proportion to increases in productivity. Otherwise there is the danger that consumption will not keep pace with output.

The age of automation accelerates the need for greater comprehension and farsightednes on the part of both managements and labor. For example, rapid change-over times and greatly decreased inventories require more alertness and greater technical knowledge of managers than ever before. Furthermore as productive processes and factory layouts are changed the problem of determining managerial responsibility may change. In some cases automation may cause confusion of responsibility as formerly discontinuous, specialized fuctions are tied together in a continuous flow process. In other cases the improved communications system may make responsibility easier to fix and buck passing among departments harder to get away with.

Electronic computers increase the amount of knowledge, the accuracy of information and the speed with which it is obtainable, thus giving management a much clearer picture of its over-all operation. By making knowledge of the consequences of alternative courses of action readily available business operations in the future can be conducted more rationally than in the past. Unprofitable operations or products can be more quickly discovered and credit managers will be able to follow the changes in financial ratios day by day. Collective bargaining and product pricing will be based on a greater volume of accurate information so that areas of controversy will be narrowed and conflicts based on misunderstandings of facts will decline.

Automation can be expected to affect the location pattern of industries in several ways. First, there may be a shift in labor oriented industries. The attractiveness of low labor cost regions could be reduced, perhaps to the point of elimination. This can occur for two reasons. First, the number of workers in the automatized plant is considerably reduced thereby lessening the savings to be gained from employing cheap labor. Second, the automatized labor force is primarily constituted by skilled labor and there is usually a smaller wage differential between the skilled employees of different regions than between the semi-skilled and unskilled workers.

A second effect of automation of the location of industries is due to the possibility of an accelerated rate of obsolescence of equip-ment. There is an increased likelihood of abandonment of plants and the creation of depressed areas. If one large firm adopts auto-matic operations other firms in the industry may have to scrap or sell undepreciated machinery and adopt similar techniques or be squeezed out of the industry by the lower costs of their automatized rivals.

Entire communities could become ghost towns if this happened and although there should be no long run attempt to freeze existing industrial patterns nevertheless some kind of direct assistance may become necessary to mitigate the most acute hardships in these dis-tressed areas. Some of this aid could come by requiring the firms which are seeking lower cost locations to bear a larger share of the social costs of their operations. For example, the costs of moving workers and their families, earlier retirement under pension plans, increased unemployment pay and retraining programs should be borne by largely the firm. Industries composed of large and ex-panding firms could guarantee annual wages. Other costs would have to be borne by the government. For example, a greatly expanded free employment service would facilitate mobility and reduce frictional unemployment. Public works projects in distressed locations would provide jobs which would generate the purchasing power necessary to sustain business.

Third, automation is likely to affect location and operations by causing a substitution of process methods of production in place of job methods. Thus there may be more emphasis on the use of gasses, liquids, electric power and pure compounds and less emphasis on natural products, crude mixtures and solids, since the latter are less adaptable to the flow of automatic processes. This may result in the displacement of large numbers of workers many of whom have long experience, seniority rights and low mobility. A need may arise here to induce multi-plant firms to provide transfer rights among their various operations. Furthermore, as firms adopt auto-matic process types of operations the necessity of constant production arises. One logical extension of this concept of the business firm is, of course, the guaranteed annual wage, which has become eco-nomically justifiable in many industries now because of the necessity of maintaining full production, full employment and the mass purchasing power to sustain them.

In the past, as machinery has replaced men in production, energy has been released which was partly absorbed by an expansion of employment in travel, entertainment, and personal services. Automation should accelerate this process.

Although the rate and extent of unionization probably will not decline directly as a result of automation, there will undoubtedly continue to be a relative expansion of employment in the service activities, a large proportion of which have been resistant to union organization in the past. While there is still considerable room for organization of production workers in the economy, this shift in the employment pattern suggests a possible expansion of areas which are more difficult to organize. For example, total employment has risen considerably since 1948, but employment in the increasingly automatic oil refining industry (which is highly unionized) has fallen from 147,000 to 137,000 since that time, although refinery production rose 22%. Several other basic industries have witnessed a decline of production workers and a great increase in engineers and technicians already.

Mechanization in general and automation in particular have three consequences for the demand for skills in the labor force. First, some existing skills are rendered obsolete. Second, some existing skills are diluted by a further division of labor. Third, there will be a demand for new skills, usually of a higher order. This last effect seems likely to predominate so that the over-all result will be to replace lower skills with higher ones. However, the net effect on individual workers is likely to be a downgrading unless they can be retrained in new skills. So far automation has not caused any significant over-all unemployment because skilled workers have been retrained in temporary or less skilled jobs. This kind of "hidden unemployment" is often overlooked in the total employment statistics.

Thus automation, unlike mechanization in general, results in long run upgrading of the labor force as routine and uninteresting jobs are eliminated and more responsible and challenging jobs are created. There will be an increase in the demand for highly skilled maintenance men, for example, and the ratio of managers to employees will probably increase because of the increased value of the equipment and the increased scope of the work process under any one manager's supervision.

But these new jobs require more education and training. The already critical shortage of engineers, for example, is bound to get worse unless business firms can become aware that it is in their own economic self-interest to endow colleges and universities and provide more scholarships for the tens of thousands of deserving young people who cannot afford to go to college.

Perhaps the most widely discussed economic effect of automation has been technological unemployment. Fear has been expressed that the greatly reduced labor requirements of automatic factories will lead to a persistent shortage of job opportunities in the economy. As an economy-wide problem this argument may be overdrawn for several reasons. First, automation will probably be limited to industries which employ, at the most, 25% of the labor force, yet this is the most highly organized sector. Second, automatic controls do not replace the labor force entirely, although in terms of labor hours there is a considerable saving. As routine clerical and operative jobs are abolished, new maintenance and technical jobs are created which go far toward offsetting the loss of former jobs. Third, extensive training and educational programs will be required as the labor force is upgraded and these will to some extent counteract unemployment by delaying entry into the labor market.

In spite of these mitigating factors, however, the severity of technological unemployment on individuals affected should not be underestimated. Those who disparage fears of technological unemployment often assume the existence of a self-adjusting labor market. However, there is a real danger that imperfections in the labor market will seriously delay absorption of the displaced workers.

The barriers to labor mobility have always been great but even in the face of increasing concentration of capital it is likely that labor is more mobile and flexible today than ever before. Cheap transportation, improved communication and the disintegration of family and community ties, which specialization and industrialization have encouraged, all tend to make for labor flexibility among firms in the same industry or firms offering similar jobs. However, movement among occupations, particularly to more highly skilled jobs, entails great costs which individual workers cannot normally bear. Yet this is exactly the kind of mobility which automation will require. It is not necessary that all workers be equally sensitive to changes in the demand for labor or differences in opportunities. A highly mobile minority in each occupational group will usually preserve the necessary flexibility of supply except where there are structural changes taking place such as automation may produce. The individual rewards for mobility, and penalties for immobility, seem likely to increase. This will favor young, aggressive workers with few family responsibilities and discriminate against older, more settled workers. It also may encourage the opportunists and the irresponsible as against the more stable elements in the work force.

There is no reason why labor should be more mobile, flexible and willing to assume the enormous risks of economic dislocation than the other components of production—capital, management and natural resources—which are to varying degrees organized, concentrated and immobilized. Indeed sacrifices made by other factors of production in participating in a competitive market are ordinarily much less than those made by labor. The possible loss of a speculative profit or, at most, the loss of an investment which businessmen, bankers or property-owners may suffer is usually not as severe a personal hardship as the loss of livelihood to a worker. The worker has not his, or someone elses, money at stake, but his life, and his children's lives, on the auction block of the commercial market.

In summary, the long run, over-all outlook for labor as a result of automation is good. However, the short run, specific problems of expensive geographical movement, loss of seniority, obsolescence of skills and so on may be acute. Therefore, there may arise a more urgent need to reduce frictional unemployment and provide guarantees against general unemployment. These cost little if the general unemployment doesn't arise and may save billions in lost production and untold human misery if it does.

Thus public policies should be designed to protect workers against possible personal hardships resulting from economic dislocations and maintain a high and stable level of production and employment. There will be many to reply that such policies will destroy our precious freedoms. In response, and in conclusion, I can only observe that the controversy is more semantic than real.

Abraham Lincoln once said that freedom seldom means the same thing to a wolf that it means to a lamb. Build a shelter to protect the lambs and the wolves howl that the lambs have lost their freedom. Of course social services and collective bargaining restrict some kinds of freedom but they may safeguard or create other kinds of freedom of greater importance. Unemployment and insecurity can destroy freedom more effectively than laws and regulations can. Freedom to change jobs requires that there be other jobs to change to. In fact, the freedom to make a living, to pursue happiness, and to enjoy the blessings of democracy in a highly industrialized economy requires full employment and some degree of individual job security. Only stability and prosperity can insure that everyone will have the economic freedom upon which political democracy must rest. Automation can make the prosperity possible but at the same time it makes the stability indispensible. It becomes the responsibility of everyone, particularly business and government since they make the basic economic decisions of the country, to insure that the great benefits of automation are used constructively to provide a better life for all people. If this is done, automation can provide the increased productivity to eliminate the poverty which still grips a fourth of our population. If not—if the benefits of automation are not equitably distributed—then man may become, as Norbert Wiener has observed, "an afterthought of business."

# LABOR'S STAKE

WALTER P. REUTHER, *President, Congress of Industrial Organizations:*

We in the CIO sponsored the National Conference on Automation because we sincerely believe that there is a great need in America for free, honest and frank public discussion and study of the problems automation has raised.

We have said many times that we welcome automation and that we are going to encourage the expeditious development of this new technology, just as we encouraged the development of other phases of our technical development. But we are going to insist, as free citizens in our great and wonderful democracy that responsible national policies be devised to insure that this new-found power will be used with a sense of moral and social responsibility in terms of the needs of the whole community.

It is within the frame-work of this basic philosophy that we in the CIO approach the related problems. We have been disturbed in recent months by the fact that around these problems—automation and the question of how we, as a free people, can so shape our national policies so that we might maintain full employment and full production in peacetime—too often we get a great deal more heat than light. Instead of discussing such problems intelligently and rationally and coming to grips with the facts, as free people need to do, we have found that time and time again some people raise ideological windmills to do battle with.

When the CIO began talking about the question of full employment, we were honored with the tag of "prophets of doom and gloom." And when we raised the question of automation, we were called scare-mongers. That was the term that Secretary of Commerce Weeks used.

We in the CIO believe that our free enterprise system has been the vehicle upon which the American people have ridden together to the highest living standards enjoyed by any peoples in the world. We believe in the free enterprise system, and we shall defend it. But given that belief, we believe also it must be made socially responsible. It must reflect the basic needs of all of the people. Because, unless it does, it cannot meet the challenge and the test, both economically and morally, that any economic system must meet in order to justify its continuation and the support of the people.

We would like to say to the self-appointed defenders of the free enterprise system that, if the greatness of this system is founded upon the idea of

45

competition in the market place of commodities, they ought to recognize that you cannot have a free market place for commodities unless you defend the free market place of ideas in America.

If we are going to defend competition in the market place between commodities, we need to defend competition in the market place between ideas. It is in that spirit that we believe that a full, frank and public discussion of automation can shed light in place of heat upon this pressing national problem.

Now we believe that discussion of automation ought to include respect for the other fellow's right to differ. But differences in a free society ought to reflect facts, not fancy. They ought to be based upon principles, not upon prejudices. And we ought to come to grips with the problem in the spirit of recognizing that maybe the other fellow has some claim to knowledge about the problem and has a right to pursue his claim to that knowledge within the free market place of ideas in which all of us together must find the answers to the problems. In our free society, getting that measure of social responsibility and moral responsibility within the economic equation that determines the shape and the future of our economy is essential to the survival of our free enterprise system.

It is in that spirit that we in the CIO approach the question of automation. We believe that the problems of automation must be faced not on the basis of complacency on one extreme, or panic on the other. There is a middle ground that recognizes the economic facts of life and attempts to appraise these facts in terms of human and social values.

If we do that we can meet the challenge. We can realize the almost unlimited opportunities for human betterment that lie ahead if we can bring into moral balance man's great technical movement forward, which goes forward at an ever accelerated rate, and the translation of that great technical progress into the present-day currency of the basic values that we, as free people, believe in.

Automation is the second phase of the industrial revolution that started with James Watt's simple steam engine. It is the second phase because it brings into our developing technology a new element that was completely absent from the first phase of the industrial revolution. The first crude steam engine was an effort on the part of man to substitute mechanical power for human power and human muscle. From the crude beginnings until the rise of the mass production plants that have characterized the auto industry and other great industries, we had an extension and development to an even higher plane of his simple idea of the substitution of mechanical power for human power.

Automation brings in a new element which marks the beginning of the second phase of the industrial revolution. In addition to substituting mechanical power for human power, it substitutes mechanical judgment for human judgment, except that the mechanical judgment can be made infallible and human judgment which it replaces, is not infallible. It is the combination and synchronizing of these two elements that really gives us some appreciation of the tremendous possibilities that automation opens up to the people of our country, and ultimately, to the people of the world. That is why we need to understand that automation is not just the extension of an old process. It is an extension of the old with a revolutionary new element—the element of mechanical judgment in substitution for human judgment.

It also must be recognized that the major impact of the first days of the industrial revolution—the substitution of mechanical power for human muscle—was upon the people doing manual or physical work, essentially in areas of production. The impact of automation is much broader. In terms of its economic and social implications it is much more challenging. Its opportunities are far greater because the impact of this new technology upon every phase of our complex economy will be tremendous.

Already obsolete are those auto plants that can turn out a complete engine block fully machined, in fifteen minutes. They are obsolete because there are plans on the drawing board to do the same job in ten minutes, with not a human hand touching it.

We already have in the auto industry a body stamping plant in which two fellows feed the steel in at one end and the finished parts come out the other. In the television industry, they can assemble a television set without a human hand touching it. The Metropolitan Life Insurance Company can automate an office easier than you can automate a factory. This is going to have a tremendous impact upon our white collar workers. No industry is immune to the impact of automation.

This whole technological ability to capture an idea and store it in the memory of a machine and to recall that memory based upon an impulse, fed into the machine by a tape, or by some other technical process, is an idea that opens up doors that heretofore have been closed to technology. Automation now makes it possible to take a recording of Caruso, to capture the tone qualities of every note, and to store those qualities in the memory of a machine; today a song writer can write a new hit, transfer it to a tape, put the tape through the machine, and have that machine call out of its memory the tone qualities of Caruso. The net result is that Caruso can be made to sing a song written twenty years after he died.

James Carey points out that today two workers can assemble a thousand radios which required two hundred workers before. Some people say that the 198 displaced fellows will be employed in making the machine that laid them off. Now that sounds good, but it isn't true.

When the General Motors Corporation has a billion dollar expansion program, of which 98% is not expansion but modernization in terms of automation and the new technology, does anyone believe that this firm is going to find a way to displace workers directly involved in the production of cars and then turn around and pull them back into the production process in terms of indirect labor in making the machines?

You can say a lot of things about General Motors, but it is not known as being a great philanthropic organization. It certainly is not introducing automation just to lessen the human burden on the production line. There is a net gain to the corporation, economicwise. As the competitive struggle intensifies, so the drive for more advanced technology is stimulated in order to reduce the unit cost of production by reducing the labor cost of that unit in the production process. There is a net gain, or otherwise the economic incentives are not there. In some situations there have been net gains of 25% of the total labor savings.

In some situations there has been a greater gain. In other situations there has been a lesser gain. But there is a total net gain; that fact is inescapable.

Take the electronics industry, one of the key industries in the whole development of automation. In 1952 the production of this industry went up 275% over 1947 with only 40% more workers.

I am fairly familiar with the tooling end of the automotive industry. While I am not the greatest engineer in the world, I am also not the worst tool and die maker either; I know a little bit about this business. At the present time the M.I.T. laboratories have automatic milling machines— tool room milling machines, the machines that the tool and die makers and skilled mechanics use to make the machines that do the automatic work on the production line. The highest skilled mechanic, who has served his apprenticeship and worked 25 years in the business, can put a job on a standard Cincinnati Milling Machine, with all sorts of compound angles and all sorts of curves; he can work 500 hours on that job, machining it, and he won't make it perfect. Now the M.I.T. laboratories have an automatic milling machine through which they put a tape punched by a girl on a mathematical formula; perfection is achieved by this machine without the help of a human hand. In short, the tool industry—the makers of the machines that will automate the production workers and automate the office workers that keep the pay-roll—will not be immune to the technical impact and the displacements of the new technology.

So you get a compounding of elements in the total picture. That is why we need to discuss automation, not in terms of smear words or swear words, not in an attempt to squeeze some small partisan advantage out of the situation, but rather to look at it as men and women of good will. We have here a problem that will challenge the best that all of us have—we all stand on the same threshold.

You can be the poorest underpaid worker in the deep south, and you can be the highest paid corporation executive on Park Avenue or in Grosse Point, and you cannot escape the impact upon the structure of the society in which you live. In a world of chaos there are no social test tubes that can be made so air-tight that you can find a piece of Utopia for your own private consumption.

We need therefore to understand that together we must find the common answers to our common problems. Finding those answers will be the measure of our survival because we are at a crucial point in human history. You can put all the eloquence aside. If we, blessed as no people in the world are blessed, cannot find a way to bring into moral balance economic and material factors with moral and social and human values, then where in the world can such balance be achieved? That is why I believe we in America must of necessity lead the way in demonstrating not only the great capacity to make technical progress, but an equal capacity to use it with a sense of moral and social responsibility.

Our great dilemma in America is the fact that there is a gigantic gap between the tremendous progress we have made in the physical sciences, and our lack of ability to make comparable progress in the human and social sciences. For every competent technician who knows how to work with machines and material, you will search a long time to find a social scientist who knows how to work with people.

We need to find a way to develop the social and human "know-why" to match our technical "know-how." We need to find a way quickly; the sands of time are running low in the struggle to preserve peace and freedom in the world. Unfortunately many of the people who have the power to make decisions are so busy they don't seem to have much time to think about what they are doing. That is why we often have to rely on the people in the academic world to give us new ideas and new concepts.

I have said many times that the struggle in the world is not going to be won with guns—although I agree with the 99% of the American people who feel we need to be strong with guns, strong enough to have the power to stop the despicable forces of aggression wherever they may raise their ugly heads. Nevertheless, we have to recognize that the only struggle we can win is a struggle in terms of positive values. No one can win a struggle of negative values in terms of war in the day of the H-bomb.

If we can somehow find a way to shift the center of balance so that the struggle between the free world and the world of Communist tyranny will not be in terms of who can make the biggest H-bomb—nobody can win that struggle—but, rather, who can take the genius of modern science and technology and give tangible expression to that genius in terms of living standards, in terms of a fuller measure of human dignity and human happiness, we can give leadership to that struggle and we can win.

For the first time in the history of human civilization we are at that point where we can begin to master man's physical environment. We can begin to use the blessings which the good Lord has bestowed upon us in such abundance to feed and clothe and house mankind, to meet man's basic economic and material needs, and, having done that we can begin to facilitate man's growth as a social and cultural and spiritual being, which is the real meaning of life.

We have to recognize that economics is not the end product: economics is the means to the end. Within the glory of his own individual personality man is the expression, the highest expression, of the Creator. What we need to do is to find a way to free mankind of the chains that have bound him to economic slavery so that he can begin to grow spiritually and intellectually and culturally.

In demonstrating our ability to reflect our great technical power and our economic resources in terms of human progress and human happiness we will create a power that will be more decisive than all of the H-bombs that we will ever make.

Now the Communists have said that because we have competing economic pressure groups between labor and management and big business and small business we as a free people cannot develop the singleness of purpose, the sense of unity, the common denominators essential to hold us together and give us the cohesion in terms of positive values that we demonstrate so well in terms of common fears and hatreds and in terms of negative pressures of war. I believe the Communists are wrong. I believe their whole conception that history is written exclusively in terms of man's struggle for material values can be proved completely wrong. We can prove it not by pious declarations, but by working together, free labor and free management, free people, free government, in a free society, finding the answers to our basic problems.

Now some people say, "Well, in the long run, everything will come out o. k., and we will all live happily together." If we could afford that kind of dangerous and unrealistic type of wishful thinking, I should be most happy to drink deeply of it. The fact is that in the world in which we live neither peace nor war is inevitable; neither is the prosperity made possible by our technology. We will get what we work for. We will get what we plan for. We will get what we have the vision to see.

That is why we of the C. I. O. say, "Let's talk about our problems as free people. Let's work to try to find common answers to our problems." There are no simple answers. There are no magic formulas. There are no panaceas. But there are answers if we have the good sense to look for them together. No one can find any answers in a little comfortable compartment unrelated to the welfare of his neighbor. There is only one compartment and that is the compartment in which all of us live together.

Remember that America has fashioned its greatness by doing what the men of little faith said was impossible. We can meet the challenge of automation, we can translate the unlimited possibilities for betterment in the lives of people not only in America but people everywhere. But it will take some practical, down-to-earth, sensible action on the part of all of us.

First we hail and we commend the action of the Joint Congressional Committee on the Economic Report, for having indicated, based upon the request of the C. I. O., that they would study the broader impact of automation. We believe that effort is part of the broader effort of implementing the purpose and the meaning of the Employment Act of 1945. We are going to cooperate with that Committee. We hope that every other segment of our free society will try to do the same so that that Committee can have access to the basic knowledge now available in this important field.

Second, we would like to recommend to the Committee that it perform a function which we believe no private economic group, either labor or management, can do. We recommend that the Joint Committee try to act as a clearing house through which we can assemble and make available to people generally the total knowledge available in this field.

The General Motors people know what they are doing and they probably know generally about what the automotive industry is doing. General Electric knows what is happening in its plants and what is happening in the electrical industry. But no one has the total picture· of what is going on in the whole field of automation. A Congressional Committee is the logical place to begin to coordinate and pull together the sum of our knowledge in this field. Only as we have access to that total knowledge can we begin to evaluate the impact of automation upon our economy and upon the social structure of our free society.

Third, we need to get down to a retraining program for our workers. The impact of this problem will not be an even impact; it will be uneven as it affects individual workers and their families, as it affects industry, and as it affects the community in which those industries are located.

To meet the problem of the workers, we have to find some way to cushion the economic impact, even if in the long pull those workers who are directly displaced by automation are absorbed indirectly in the economic system. We have to protect them during the interim period, during which the relocation and the retraining takes place, so that the individual worker and his family, or the individual community which may have a plant which is closed down, will not carry a disproportionate share of the economic and social cost of technological progress.

If we are going to train workers, we have to know for what we are training them. You cannot have a training program in the abstract. If a worker is laid off in a radio plant because two workers can now turn out a thousand sets a day where we needed two hundred workers before, 198 workers displaced by the automated line have to be retrained to do something else. Therefore, you have to know what jobs will open up for them, what skills are required to qualify them for those jobs, etc. This is not something that one company or one industry can meet.

Then you have the question of plant relocation. I think it will be accepted without challenge that on the whole it is much more economic good sense to build a new plant in which to place an automated line than to try to adapt that line to an existing facility. The experience in the auto industry shows clearly that in almost every case they try to get new plants where that is at all feasible.

Where will they locate the new plants? That is not purely an economic question. That is a question which must be answered in terms of its social effects. Unless the location of the new plant is made with a sense of moral and social responsibility, in terms of the people displaced or the community in which the people who are displaced by automation live, it can lead to a very serious problem. Permit me to cite an example. Ford built a new automatic stamping plant in Cleveland. It took place at a time when the labor force was expanding and it did not create any problem in the existing plants. If that had taken place in a time of stable employment or declining employment, it could have created some critical problems. Plant location is, then, a social question which management must meet as part of its responsibility in our free enterprise system.

We also have of course, the problem of plant location in terms of national security, the dispersement policy of ocr government, strategic considerations of wartime conditions.

Another item which the Congressional Committee ought to give recognition to, and work on, is the question of increased productivity resulting from the automated technology. In this case, they have to measure two factors: the increased productivity per man-hour and the increase in the gross national product. Both are related factors affecting our economic future. We have to find a way to achieve a dynamic expanding balance between greater productive power and greater purchasing power within the hands of people.

If we maintain that dynamic expanding balance, which is the key to the future of our free economy, then automation will not create any serious problems if there is an adjustment to take the impact off the workers and the community.

In terms of the technical progress we have made, in terms of the unrealized potential of technical progress, the present 75c minimum wage is exceedingly unrealistic. It should be raised to $1.25 per hour. All economic values are relative. You cannot measure $1.25 an hour against some economic factor existing in some sort of academic vacuum. You have to measure $1.25 per hour in terms of the level of our technology, the productivity per man-hour, and the potential of our gross national product. For obvious reasons, the minimum wage law can be an important factor in maintaining the dynamic balance between productive power and purchasing power.

We ultimately ought to get to a shorter work week. But here again we ought to get to a shorter week not in an effort to escape the problems of automation and economic abundance. We ought to get a shorter work week on the basis of a rational decision at that point in the development of our society where we have the material things we need to make a normal, healthy life for people, and we want more leisure. We will get more leisure by a shorter work week.

All of us can agree that culture in most societies is the by-product of leisure. But culture cannot be the by-product of leisure if leisure means unemployment and enforced involuntary idleness. Leisure must mean more time to do the things that free individuals choose to do in the pursuit of those non-economic activities that give them opportunity for growth as people, as social beings, as spiritual beings—but they have to have the opportunity to pursue these values within the framework of economic security and material well-being. Real leisure means leisure through a rational reduction in the work week, in which we protect the economic position of workers.

Now one argument is that automation will not create any serious unemployment problems because there is going to be a tapering off in the birth rate. Therefore it is contended the growth in the labor force is not going to continue to move up as fast as before. Let us, for the moment, assume that is correct. What actually happens, of course, is they chop the labor force off at the bottom by saying there are 9,000,000 people in the universities and schools. Then they chop it off at the top and say we are requesting earlier retirement. The net result is a reduced labor force. And then they say there is no problem.

That is all very wonderful, but how do you make it possible for more people, more youngsters in America, to have that greater education opportunity which will keep them out of the labor force? You cannot do that by wishful thinking. Right now we have a deficit of 390,000 elementary school rooms. By 1960, we will have a 600,000 deficit if we don't do something about it. How many young people can go to school, to the higher seats of learning, under such conditions, so that we can develop the great, untapped fountain of genius which is American youth?

I am in favor of paring the labor force on both ends, on the low end by giving American youth that degree of educational opportunity which will facilitate the maximum mental growth of every child, regardless of his race or creed or color. But you have to do things to bring about that great day. You cannot just wish for them.

I am for making it possible for people to retire earlier, on a voluntary basis, if they choose to do so, with the kind of economic security that will give them that measure of dignity and happiness in their evening years to which they are entitled. But you cannot wish for that. We had to fight hard to get even minimum pension benefits. And we had to fight hard for twelve years to get one penny of increase in the level of Social Security benefits.

In short, it's not enough to glibly say, "We will shave down the labor force by retiring more people earlier, and keep more people out of the labor force by keeping them in school longer." You have to do something about these things. They will not happen automatically.

Unemployment compensation has to be brought to realistic levels to cushion the impact of dislocations when they take place. Living standards can be raised a great deal. We have really just made a beginning. Much is possible if we gear potential abundance to the needs of the people. Right now the auto workers and the electrical workers are starting a crusade for a guaranteed annual wage. How will this affect the problems of automation? First of all, such a wage will sustain the purchasing power of workers during periods of temporary lay-offs, thus avoiding a compounding of economic factors in which unemployment breeds more unemployment. Second, it will mean, when automation does replace a worker, that during the period of his guarantee, he can be retrained and go through the process of being relocated without the impact of unemployment being a burden on him and his family. And third, it will be a powerful economic incentive—and that is supposed to be the power house that drives forward the great thing we call free enterprise. So when the management people decide to invest a billion dollars in new plants with automation, they will build those plants and time the flow of the new technology with a sense of responsibility, knowing that if they don't do well, in terms of their broad planning, they will have to guarantee the workers displaced an annual wage during that period. In the long pull that will have a tremendous impact upon stimulating a sense of social responsibility that must parallel in our free society the right of private economic groups to make basic economic decisions. In a free society you cannot have power without moral responsibility. For all economic power that anyone exercises, whether it be labor or management or government, there must of necessity be a corresponding moral obligation to use that power in the interest of all of the people who make up society.

We believe that automation and the abundance it makes possible ought to be used more realistically in terms of economic aid programs. We ought to all recognize that just as peace and freedom are indivisible values, just as we have to fight on the fronts where these values are challenged in order to defend peace and freedom in the world, that ultimately the world cannot defend peace and freedom if there are large cesspools of injustice anywhere because the Communists will exploit those cesspools and transform poverty into power for their own special purposes. Therefore, as a matter of enlightened self-interest in assessing our moral obligations, we need to give more to fight poverty and hunger in the world, so that more people can have the material income they need so they can begin to develop some of these other values that we believe in.

It is in the light of these overall considerations that we of the C. I. O. called the National Conference on Automation. We stand on the threshold of a new technology. We believe that there is and there must be enough good sense, enough good will, enough competent sense of morality and social responsibility on the part of labor and management and government, of educators, and the men and clergymen—on the part of all of us put together —to be able to build a better tomorrow. We believe that the values we as a free people believe in can be made to grow and flower. We believe the American people can begin to shape the world in the image of their hopes and aspirations and dreams.

NAT GOLDFINGER, *Associate Director of Research, C.I.O.:*

According to newspaper reports, there are some persons who disparage the new technology, who feel that automatic controls and the likelihood of automatic factories and automatic offices are phantoms dreamed up by so-called scaremongers like Walter Reuther. But there can hardly be any doubt that the new technology is here—not only in the minds of academicians and so-called scaremongers, but already in operation in scattered parts of the economy.

This development is, of course, in its early stages. But automatic controls, electronic computers, new concepts of production processes and work flow have been and are being introduced into factories and offices almost daily.

Professor Campbell tells us that "after we know what we want to make, and how we can make it, the sequence of operations can be unified, mechanized and made automatic." And also that "any sequence of mechanical manipulations that a man can make with his hands and feet, however simple or complex, can be made by a machine . . . The robots and the computers, the automatic factories and the automatic offices are . . . replacing the hand tools that served man a century ago, and the simple power tools and desk calculations that served him recently." Mr. Diebold refers to the Second Industrial Revolution.

This new technology is a continuation of man's struggle to control his environment. Naturally, it is not new in the sense of a sudden full-blown appearance; it rests upon innumerable previous theoretical developments and practical applications. Yet, it is a radical departure in its use of new techniques arising from electronics and electrical engineering and in its widespread—perhaps, universal—applicability.

It is the function of those in the field of engineering science to develop new and improved tools and production processes. These tools and production processes may be socially neutral in the laboratory. When placed into practical operation, however, they are used in connection with the production of goods and services; they can no longer be viewed as neutral since economic and social consequences flow from their application. It is inevitable, therefore, for society to be concerned with technology. Furthermore, it seems to me to be the obligation of society as a whole—including the engineers—to be concerned with the social and economic implications of technological change, especially of the drastic change of the new technology we are discussing.

Technological change always has some degree of social and economic impact. The introduction of new and improved machinery of a conventional type into a plant frequently displaces labor, increases productivity, or makes necessary changes in skills, job content and wage rates. The degree of impact from such technological change may be slight, the number of people involved is usually small—although it must be underscored that even such impact is real for the people directly affected. What kind of impact may be expected from the introduction of the new technology?

While there is general and widespread agreement that the new technology is a reality and a radical departure from present conventional techniques, it is in the attempt to appraise its probable social and economic impact that various divergent views appear.

One anticipated cushion to the possibility of widespread labor displacement resulting from the introduction of automation, is presented by Mr. Diebold as the growth of firms that manufacture automation equipment. He tells us that there are more than 1,000 companies engaged wholly, or partly, in such manufacture and that their aggregate output last year was over $3,000,000,000. But there is some vital information required before we can join Mr. Diebold in believing that the production of automation equipment is already creating any large number of new jobs.

How many of the 1,000 firms are new ones? Certainly, not General Electric or IBM. What did these firms produce before they engaged in the production of automation equipment? Have these firms been adding to their work-force as rapidly as the output of automation equipment rises?

Furthermore, the value of aggregate output tells us nothing about employment. Had Mr. Diebold even given us the increasing value of aggregate output, we would still lack any information concerning jobs. Increases in manhour output can give us increases in aggregate production, without any expansion of employment.

Productivity in the automation equipment industries is rising rapidly. Automation is being applied in those industries, too. Certainly, it is an expanding industry. But will it expand sufficiently and with rapidity to provide enough new jobs to make the displacement problem of no concern?

A Labor Department study of the electronics industry two years ago points to the industry's rapidly increasing productivity and states that "trends toward automation may result in the greatest reduction in unit manhours in the industry's history during the next few years." When we examine the employment figures for wage and salary earners (not production workers, alone) in the industry group in which automation equipment is largely produced, we fail to find any substantial increases between 1952 and 1954. In 1952 there were 1,100,000 wage and salary employees in the electrical machinery industry; in 1953 the figure rose to 1,200,000, but in 1954 it dropped back to 1,100,000. Although the electrical machinery industry produces many items in addition to automation equipment, I think these figures have a distinct bearing on the point.

Output and sales of automation equipment are expanding. But it seems rather clear that employment in the production of automation equipment is not rising at a rate anywhere close to the increases in output and sales. I doubt whether employment in the automation equipment industry will expand fast enough to provide new jobs for any substantial proportion of workers displaced by automated equipment elsewhere in the economy. As I see it, Mr. Diebold's point in this connection is a weak reed to rest on.

Mr. Diebold also tells us that "the pressure on the job market will be lessening during the next decade—the period when the great changes of automation will be made." Peter Drucker has made similar statements. Is there any foundation for this view? Mr. Diebold stresses the impact of retirement of the aged on the labor force and Mr. Drucker emphasizes the impact of extended education—which tend to reduce the participation rate in the labor force of both younger and older people. But both observers seem to ignore the continuing trend towards an increasing participation of women in the labor forces.

Furthermore, we are entering a period when the growth of the labor force will begin to feel the effects of the rising birthrate since 1939. More young people will be looking for jobs in the coming decade than in recent years. The Bureau of the Census has taken these various trends into consideration in its projections of labor force growth into the future. These projections point to an accelerating growth of the labor force in the coming decade, precisely when, according to Mr. Diebold, "the great changes of automation will be made." The Census figures (from Current Population Reports, Series P-50, No. 42) for average annual increases in the labor force are as follows:

| | | |
|---|---|---|
| 1950-1955 | 698,000 | 1.1% |
| 1955-1960 | 866,000 | 1.2% |
| 1960-1965 | 1,172,000 | 1.6% |

This means that the labor force, which has been growing at an average annual rate of about 1.1%, will be expanding at accelerating rates within the coming ten years, at the same time that productivity will be rising rapidly, if automation becomes widespread. I am not suggesting that the Census Bureau is infallible, but I do think that a critical evaluation of these figures and the projection of a different series is necessary before we can conclude that the Census Bureau is entirely wrong. If the Census projection of an accelerating growth of the labor force is substantially correct, then the problem of labor displacement cannot be shrugged off, but must be faced with forethought and planning. And I have seen no evidence to indicate that the Census Bureau's projection is basically incorrect.

Both Professor Cambell and Mr. Diebold suggest that the introduction of automation should be speeded up. Professor Campbell says that "we may not get increased productive and service capacity soon enough to meet our needs." Mr. Diebold likewise underscores the idea that "our needs increase continually."

True enough, but between the need for goods and services on the one hand and the purchase of goods and services on the other, falls the shadow of some unfortunate economic factors, such as jobs, income, savings and credit.

It is not true that the needs of the American people were less in the 1930's than they were in the 1920's. Yet, we produced less in the 1930's and we wasted manpower and productive capacity. And were our needs any less in 1954, when unemployment rose and production, sales and employment fell, as compared to 1953?

Needs in themselves do not produce customers. Rather, it is needs backed up with cash or credit.

It is precisely this point that has many of us concerned. Will we adopt social and economic policies that will make it possible to provide rapidly growing markets based on increasing consumer purchasing power to match the rapid growth of output during the transition to the widespread use of the new technology? Will the social and economic policies of private groups and government be adequate to sustain economic growth and full employment while the introduction of automated equipment raises productivity and dislocates part of the labor force?

Perhaps, I have sounded pessimistic. This is not my intention.

All of us at this table welcome automation; we rejoice at the tremendous advances in output, in national strength, in leisure, in working and living conditions that the new technology makes possible.

Nevertheless, I think it essential that we face the issues squarely, that if problems seem likely to arise, we attempt to examine them now instead of dodging them.

We cannot just go ahead and *assume* that full employment will be maintained during the transition to the new technology. We cannot *assume* that our desires—our needs—will be fulfilled because we wish it so.

Terms such as "obituary accounting" are of no help in seeking policies that will make possible the rapid expansion of new job opportunities to provide employment for young people entering the labor force, as well as for those who may be displaced by automated equipment.

There is no automatic self-adjusting mechanism to provide a rapidly growing number of new jobs. Neither is there any electronic control mechanism to provide rapidly growing consumer markets to sustain full production and full employment, if the output of goods soars with the widespread introduction of automation.

What is required is the development of adequate social and economic policies that will stimulate the rapid growth of markets and new jobs, that will minimize social dislocations and cushion the blows that may befall families or communities as a result of the widespread introduction of the new technology.

In trying to appraise the possible and probable impact of the new technology on society and the economy, a cross-fertilization of information, data and ideas is needed, not merely from the various academic disciplines of the sciences and social sciences, but also from people of the various groups in society—such as organized labor, management and government. If we who are not scientific technicians are to appraise the implications of the new technology, those from the field of engineering science must assist us.

There are a host of questions to be raised and some answers—even tentative answers—must be developed. The limited time of this conference will make possible the asking of only a few of these questions and partial replies to an even smaller number. I think this points up the necessity for further examination of these issues by private groups and government.

JACK CONWAY, *Assistant to President, United Automobile Workers:*

The trade unionist must look upon the problems accompanying automation in terms of the impact upon workers—the impact of radical changes in the factory as well as changes in employment and wages. And as the bread-winners are affected, so also are the lives of their families.

There have been, of course, over the years, tremendous developments occurring in the mass production industries. The automobile industry, for example, has been characterized by a general reduction in unit manpower in various kinds of plant operations. This has been the result of technological improvements and innovations called automation. Automation is usually associated with the perfection of better machinery operating at higher speeds and requiring more careful attention on the part of the operator. Over the past two or three months, we have had a public relations controversy on this whole question of automation. As Professor George Shultz has pointed out, it is associated with the sociology of this general subject.

We have some rather important collective bargaining sessions under way in the auto industry at the present time. The guaranteed annual wage is on the bargaining table as a major demand. In addition, there is a wage demand tied to an increase in the size of our annual improvement factor which in turn is tied in with the rate of technological improvement in our economy. I think that Mr. Northrup expressed the situation very well when he recently said on a platform I happened to share: "The man who coined the term 'automation' will probably go down in history as the man who turned technological improvements and technological developments over to the public relations people." That is essentially what has happened.

For about two weeks following the release of the UAW statement on automation, there was a kind of stunned silence. And then out came the generals and admirals to propound the new management line. First they said there was no such thing as automation. General Motors issued instructions that automation was a dirty word and no longer should be used by its personnel. Commerce Secretary Weeks hit the public press with statements about "scaremongers and economic illiterates." Labor Secretary Mitchell, without his wires properly crossed, conceded, before a Congressional Committee that there is such a thing as technological displacement. Subsequently, however, he changed his mind a bit.

I think the four principal speakers at the National Automation Conference have made a genuine contribution. They have brought to this conference four points of view which indicate there are some differences of opinion. This is proper and to be expected because we have asked people to come here without regard to their personal points of view. There are certain conclusions, however, which I think can be drawn from the remarks of all the speakers.

Number One: Our language needs some technological improvement. We use the same terms, but they mean different things. For example, I think we ought to stop talking about the long run and the short run. In the long run, we say, things are going to be thus and so, and in the short run things are going to be this and that. When we stop to think about it, the long run is now the short run. Most of the people are talking in terms of five years, or ten years at the most.

In this day and age, we are making some basic changes in our lives during the course of a normal lifetime. Our children are already so far ahead of us that we are becoming obsolete in our ideas. So we really have to take a more careful look at our own terminology as we begin to look in more detail at the question of automation and technological improvements.

I think there is another point where there can be common agreement. The American economy now is reaping the benefits of the forced draft of World War II developments. With eleven million people removed from our civilian labor force, and under the pressure of a gigantic war operation, the United States government established, sponsored and assisted the kind of research which led to the development of the atomic bomb and all of the subsequent developments in the field of atomic energy. In the aircraft industry and guided missile field, a tremendous amount of work was done both during World War II and since. We have to keep in mind, it seems to me, that all of these major developments have been financed at great cost by the American people and conducted under the supervision of the United States Government. The taxpayers of the United States, the people generally, have paid for these things.

There has been a revolution in the handling of materials; there has been a revolution in the whole area of marketing, transport, and distribution techniques. There has been a revolution in the controlling of machinery through the development of instruments, as a result of this government research. Industry is using new regulating equipment for peacetime purposes which was developed originally to handle fissionable and highly dangerous materials.

A third point on which there is agreement is: These new developments are now being reflected in our industrial society in the process we call automation. It may mean different things to different people, but the one thing everybody seems to be agreed upon is that the effect will be vast and far-reaching. But there I think the agreement ends.

John Diebold, in his paper, expresses the opinion that with automation will come flexibility that will enable small businesses to compete with big businesses. They will be able to compete successfully, he believes, in a rapidly changing world. Disruptive changes, while possible, are not serious, according to his analysis.

Professor Campbell, in dealing with the implications of the new technology, sees a world of industry in which the automatic machine can be and must be put to use as an extension of man's senses as man is called upon more and more to function in a climate of speed beyond his capabilities. Man's normal reaction time and muscular ability are obsolete, Professor Campbell maintains. Therefore, he believes, the introduction of automation should be encouraged and speeded up to free man from a direct tie-in to the production process.

Professor Buckingham and Senator O'Mahoney, in extremely thoughtful papers, have pointed out some of the social effects and some of the economic effects of the new technology. Very briefly, I would like to underscore just a few of them. First of all, as expressed in their papers, there is the very serious danger to small business generally because of the high initial expense of automatic equipment and the possibility that the development in various industries around our economy will be extremely uneven. Second, while automatic control devices may very well lead to decentralization, such decentralization does not necessarily lead to less concentration of ownership. Third, they point out that the huge capital requirements and the need for established markets limit entry on the part of new companies into existing fields. In my opinion this is an extremely important consideration. ✓

As the whole process of production and distribution is tightened up and becomes more and more automatic from the time the raw materials are extracted from the earth, to the time the final product is delivered to the consumer, as it becomes a continuous straight line process, it is going to become more and more difficult for new businesses to become established. Even though they have the ingenuity and perhaps the capital to break into industry, they lack the facilities to obtain and turn raw materials into finished products and to get their products distributed through this very complicated and extensive marketing process.

Another point which I think needs underscoring is that automation has the effect of speeding up of the rate of obsolescence of equipment. The automobile industry illustrates this characteristic of automation. General Motors emerged from World War II with a modern plant facility decentralized around the United States. As we frequently used to say, General Motors has its headquarters in Detroit and its hindquarters all over the United States. The Ford Motor Company, on the other hand, emerged from World War II with a highly centralized, obsolete plant. Through sharp changes over ten years with tremendous capital investment, in a market situation where it was possible to sell practically any automobile that was made, the Ford Motor Company modernized its plant. It built manufacturing and assembly establishments all over the United States, and it introduced automation into the automobile industry.

Ford Motor Company is now competitive with General Motors, but what has happened to Chrysler, and the independents? The president of the Dodge Division of the Chrysler Corporation stated recently: "The economics of automation are harsh but simple; automate or die." The Chrysler Corporation and the independents are now trying desperately to recover their place in the market by consolidation, expansion and modernization of their equipment. Automation made their facilities obsolete. More automation by Ford and General Motors may make today's new plants obsolete. And, as one observer stated, "automation in Detroit leads to unemployment in South Bend."

Another phase of this problem has been illustrated by the Ford Motor Company in deciding, in connection with its decentralization-modernization program, to locate its new foundry, engine and stamping plants in Cleveland and Buffalo. Keeping in mind that most of the ores that they will be using in the years to come will come from Labrador and not from Minnesota, that decision perhaps makes sense. The workers that went into the Buffalo and Cleveland plants are new, they are young; they do not have old habit patterns that must be changed. On the other hand, the workers in the Detroit area and in some of the other older automotive centers, where the machinery is old, have the tendency to want to stay in their communities rather than transfer with the jobs. There is a danger that these workers might become obsolete along with the factories in the older centers.

There is also a tremendous change in job content in the automated factories. I don't want to take the time here to elaborate on the kind of changes which are taking place but I can, by an illustration from the *New York Post,* indicate the nature of one problem to be faced:

"Then there are workers who can't keep up with automation. Such as Stanley Tylak. Tylak, 61 and for 27 years a job setter at Ford, was shifted from the River Rouge foundry machine shop to the new automated engine plant. He was given a chance to work at a big new automatic machine.

"Simply, straightforwardly, he told his story: 'The machine had about 80 drills and 22 blocks going through. You had to watch all the time. Every few minutes you had to watch to see everything was all right. And the machines had so many lights and switches—about 90 lights. It sure is hard on your mind.

"'If there's a break in the machine the whole line breaks down. But sometimes you make a little mistake, and it's no good for you, no good for the foreman, no good for the company, no good for the union.'

"And so Stanley Tylak, baffled by the machine he couldn't keep up with, had to take another job—at lower pay."

That is the kind of situation that can develop generally for the older workers in automated plants.

We are rapidly approaching a point, it seems to me, where the adult worker can become the forgotten man in our society. He must be given the opportunity for retraining well in advance of the change in technology. Then, when he does go on a new job he will not be frightened by the fact that it is very different from his former experience.

Almost everyone agrees that we have an appalling lack of knowledge of the consequences of automation. Because much of the current research that is going on ties back into defense work and into the general field of atomic energy, there is some control and secrecy attached to it. This explains to some extent our lack of accurate information. Only a Congressional Committee can have access to the necessary information. Such a Committee can begin to appraise the effect of this research and the development of equipment occurring under the supervision of the government. We in the labor movement certainly can't get at it. Significantly, the application of automation is mainly in the hands of giant corporations that can use this information to their advantage in bargaining situations.

We in the labor movement seem to have to go to the Supreme Court every time we want to get ordinary wage data. You can imagine the difficulty we would have trying to get data dealing with technological improvement. This is the kind of thing a Congressional Committee can handle.

It seems to me we need another federal investigation of economic concentration. We have not had that basic kind of fact-finding in this country since the T.N.E.C. We need it badly and I hope that in the process of his Congressional investigation of the implications of automation Senator O'Mahoney will again, as he did after the other investigation, raise the possibility of national charters for national corporations. Corporations are now reaching the point, as he has said, where states can no longer supervise and control them. As the Senator suggested earlier, it is apparent that we need regulations such as federal licensing of huge corporations.

Let me conclude by saying this. Great Britain has already announced that in a matter of ten years it expects to develop at least 25 percent of its total power through atomic energy installations. When the "Nautilus" made its first dive in the Atlantic Ocean not very long ago, the speed with which corporations lined up at the bar of the A.E.C. to quench their thirst reminded me of my Irish relatives in their speedy trip to the neighborhood pub to get that first cooling drink of beer after their Sunday morning attendance at church.

Many, perhaps most, of our large corporations are being licensed by the United States Government to take advantage of the research and development which has been conducted at the expense of the taxpayers during World War II and since. This is another area which a Congressional investigating committee might well take a very close look at. And while it is looking into these points it would be wise to examine the renewed emphasis on what I would call peculiar mergers, purchases and consolidations.

In our industry, the automobile companies are suddenly buying up apparently unrelated firms and concerns. They are diversifying. There may be sound reasons for this process and we should not prejudge this conduct. But I think it is the kind of thing we ought to look at very carefully. For example, it amazes me when food processing companies end up producing automatic equipment for the electronics industry.

The many interests of General Motors lead to some questionable situations. General Motors holds a contest in which they are going to pay nobly the person who can come up with the best scheme for financing highways and parking lots. The contest produces a great interest in the whole question of road building. The Government of the United States comes out with a proposal for a $101 billion road program. General Lucius Clay, who is on the Board of General Motors, ends up heading a special committee of the government to study how it should be done. In the meantime, General Motors quietly buys the Euclid Road Machinery Company and is all set to make all the equipment it takes to build all these roads.

At this conference we have focused attention on automation and its ramifications. From now on we should join with men of good will in honest and extensive investigation of automation to harness this new phenomenon for the good of all. And in the process, let's take this question out of the hands of the public relations people.

JAMES B. CAREY, *Secretary-Treasurer, CIO, and President, International Union of Electrical, Radio and Machine Workers-CIO:*

The spread of automation poses for American industry one of the greatest challenges we will have to meet. If it is handled humanely, wisely and not greedily, it can be a boon not only to industry, but to all mankind. If handled greedily, with emphasis chiefly on profits, it can be a disaster of the first magnitude.

Automation is not merely an extension of machine production. It is, instead, as great a revolution as machine production itself. While machine production displaces some workers, automation could displace *most* workers. It means production without a human hand touching the goods to be processed. It means using tapes and electric eyes and relays instead of human hands and brains. It not only produces, but also checks and tests the product.

My own industry, the electrical industry, is affected in two ways. In some of our plants we will *build* the automation equipment to be used in other plants—in steel, auto, textile and others. To that extent it will create jobs. How many we do not know. But very significantly, a report from our General Mills plant in Minneapolis indicates that this IUE-CIO employer has perfected a device to produce by automation the *automation equipment for making consumer goods.* That's like stamping out thinking machines.

A recent report in the *Wall Street Journal* declared that "Autofab," as it is called, "will assemble in a little more than a minute the same number of multiple-part electronic units that it now takes a worker a full day to assemble.  It requires only two workers and a supervisor and has a capacity of more than 200,000 assemblies a month." For the radio, TV and parts industry, automation has developed the printed circuit which does away with wiring, the use of soldering baths instead of solderers, and automatic inspection equipment.  In plants of Philco, Emerson, Motorola, Raytheon, Sylvania, RCA, Canadian Admiral, and others; automation is already far advanced.

The introduction of the "printed circuit" at the Philco plant in Sandusky, Ohio, resulted in elimination of 25% of employees on the soldering and wiring assembly line.  GE, which makes printed circuits for other industries, boasts that these circuits will reduce a company's labor force by 50%. Another change in method whereby the entire bottom of a radio is now soldered all at once in a soldering bath has resulted in only three solderers being employed by Philco instead of the previous 40.  In addition, further reduction in employment will result when Philco starts automatic production of complete radio and television chassis at this plant.

Other sections of our industry are also advancing by huge leaps in this field of automation.  Almost all companies in the lamp industry, especially Westinghouse and General Electric, have developed automatic machinery. Examples are the machines which make lamp bases four or five times faster and devices that control four or five other machines that previously were operated by a substantial number of workers.

Automation's havoc is being spread in the office, too, among tens of thousands of so-called white collar and clerical workers.  GE's "Univac" in its Louisville, Kentucky, plant not only works out the payroll for 10,000 employees, computes incentive earnings, schedules production, looks into market possibilities, but does a dozen other tasks formerly performed by perhaps hundreds of clerical workers.  Other companies are widely adopting "Univac" or versions of it.

The magazine *Automatic Control* recently asserted that if automation could reach its maximum growth in our industry, the displacement of workers could be on the order of 100 to one.  The vast potentials of automation, obviously, have just been scratched.  A prominent Harvard economist has estimated that to fully automate all plants built in 1950 would require only $600,000,000 and that American industry may be fully automated within a decade.  This means that *one* man will do at *least* the work now done by *five* men.  It is obvious that if other industries, such as automobile, steel, oil, rubber, paper, textile and others, go ahead with automation, a vast number of workers will be displaced.  The pool of unemployed could rapidly grow into a national disaster if the companies in each industry attempt to make maximum profits from this technological revolution.

The possibilities for good in automation are fabulous, with living standards for all at a higher level than ever imagined.  The possibilities for tremendous damage are equally present. Employers must realize that automation can be a Frankenstein monster unless the consuming power is generated to buy up the flood of goods resulting from automation.

Automation joined with sufficiently increased purchasing power could be a blessing that could raise the average city family income of $6393 today to more than $10,000 within five or ten years. This requires, however, that the savings from automation be shared by: (1) Cutting prices and thereby stimulating greater markets. The average home might then have two or three TV sets as it now has several radios. (2) Raising wages and increasing the purchasing power of workers. (3) Cutting hours of work without a reduction in pay. (4) Providing against layoffs through a guaranteed employment program and severance pay programs.

These are the goals organized labor must project when automation appears imminent or is initiated in our plants. In addition, there are a number of serious contractual problems that must be met; these include:

1. Obviously if a machine requires one man instead of 20 he will not receive the same incentive rate or get 20 times the pay he received previously. The danger is that one man will receive *only the same pay as before.* Companies have revised their incentive systems with the advent of automation—basing pay on so-called "machine utilization" and not production. Or else they put workers on a day-work-rate which, if anything, offers lower earnings. Generally speaking, there is no one answer to the problem, but the best approach is to establish for workers on automatic equipment *a new classification* which provides substantially higher earnings than before. *To insure that the whole plant shares the results of the increased productivity, production bonuses should also be negotiated.*

2. Many present job classifications will become obsolete with the introduction of automatic machinery. The strict application of present job-evaluation standards may *lower, not raise,* wage rates, because the tests used in existing job evaluation systems will no longer give correct results. We should, therefore, seek revisions of all such systems and job classifications taking into account the increased production and the *new type* of responsibilities involved.

3. Seniority provisions should be revised giving displaced workers a broader area of other work to which they may transfer. Contract clauses governing layoffs, promotions, and similar matters should also be rigorously re-examined.

4. Displaced workers should be either retrained by the company, receive severance pay and/or guaranteed pay when their jobs are ended. General programs of in-plant training should be established to fit workers for the new operations. As the new equipment will inevitably be more complex, automation can elevate many workers from the drudgery of repetitive machine operations. Care must be taken at the same time to see that this is not exploited for the purpose of undermining the status of skilled trades for profiteering objectives.

5. In multi-plant companies consideration should be given to intra-plant transfers with the maximum possible seniority rights.

We should request joint union-management committees to study problems arising from automation, insisting in any case that management furnish us with full information well in advance of the technological change.

The large and complex problems presented by the advent of automation —and with implications ranging far beyond the boundaries of organized labor—will constitute another historic test of the CIO's social consciousness. The problem of old age insecurity was met by the CIO's pioneering in noncontributory pensions. The problem of periodic mass unemployment will be met by the CIO's pioneering in guaranteed employment programs. And the threat of robot factories will be met—and solved—by the same kind of intellectual courage and moral militancy that the CIO has displayed in the past.

JOSEPH A. BEIRNE, *President, Communications Workers of America*

The H bomb cannot be dismissed as merely more explosive power. It has already created totally new concepts of warfare and defense. It is creating new concepts of diplomacy. It has brought to all humanity a great cloud of doubt and darkness which cannot be dispelled by mere wish-fulfillment gestures. It has caused us to place a much higher value on peace and to go to lengths never before though possible to avoid war. In the same way, the new electronic revolution cannot be dismissed as ordinary technological improvement. This revolution has been marked by new and far reaching technological concepts. Out of these concepts there has already emerged a radically new mode of production. This mode has been summed up in the term "automation."

There are those even today who would deny the challenge and the social implications of this industrial age. Seeing not quite so far as the ends of their noses, they liken a totally new production method to the development of a new automatic machine and proclaim that it will have no social impact upon us. Conveniently forgetting the depression of twenty years ago, these people point to today's employment levels as proof that technological unemployment is only a figment of the imaginations of nasty prophets of gloom and doom. If only labor will not rock the boat, we are assured, we will automatically gain from automation a world of endless profits with prosperity trickling down to even the lowliest.

Automation might well be defined as a process by which production is achieved without the intervention of direct human labor. It is the modern name for the long dreamed of robot factory, which operates with only a small force of engineers and maintenance workers. In this factory the computer or its equivalent serves as a master electronic brain, directing the flow of materials and partially finished products from machine to machine until the finished product emerges untouched by human hands. Throughout the process, electronic eyes replace human eyes in checking upon quality and faults. Human intervention takes place only infrequently when a machine part must be replaced because of breakdown or wear.

Describing automation in a special feature article in the *New York Times* of April 6, 1955, Abe Raskin, well-known journalist, had this to say:

"So fantastic are the potentialities of new control devices that it is possible to visualize acres of factory or office space in which no worker is needed. Automated equipment can process raw materials, assemble them into finished goods, package them and load them into freight cars without direct human help.

"That is not all. The automated machines can adjust to variable productive conditions, correct their own mistakes, inspect the finished product and even change their own parts when parts break down or wear out . . .

"Automated machines do not stop with telling other machines what to do; they even 'breed' new automated equipment. With magical new calculators, design data for huge machanical installations can be completed in one-fortieth of the time formerly required."

This is the future. It is a future already upon us. It is a future affecting the office worker and the service industry worker, as well as the production worker. To dismiss this development lightly as merely more technological progress is as shortsighted as dismissing the H bomb merely as more fire power.

Automation is not new to my own industry. It might be said, in fact, that the communications industry has been a proving ground for automation. The dial system long ago permitted the telephone subscriber to perform all the direct labor necessary to complete a telephone call.

In the past several years the impact of automation has become far greater than at ever before. Today the telephone office worker and the plant craftsman are being directly affected, as well as the telephone operator. New developments in telephony are making thousands of these workers as obsolete as the old-fashioned switchboard. While not all the new developments, of themselves, can be described as automation, they are directly related to this process.

Not so many years ago it was necessary to dial the operator to complete a telephone call from a city like New York or Washington to a nearby suburban town. The majority of telephone operators in such all-dial cities were employed to complete such calls. Today the subscriber completes such suburban calls, without the assistance of any operator. Long distance calls at one time required the assistance of at least two operators and, in many instances, as many as four or five. Today the great majority of all long distance calls are dialed directly by a single operator in an operation known as operator toll dial. In relatively short haul calls, such as from Washington to Baltimore, the subscriber dials directly, although an operator does come on the line for a single instant to ask the number of the calling subscriber.

Direct subscriber long distance dialing, known as subscriber toll dialing, is already a reality. Through the use of a zoning system, subscribers will soon be able to dial directly to virtually any telephone in the United States—

without the use of an operator, except in person-to-person calls where a single operator may still be required. Ultimately, even person-to-person calls may be completely automated through the use of a device affectionately nicknamed "Lil Audrey" by the Bell Telephone Laboratories.

Direct subscriber toll dialing has been made possible by an automated system known as the automatic message accounting device. Through the use of this device the calling number and city, the called number and city, the time the call is begun and the time the call is completed are recorded on a perforated tape.

Automatic billing centers where tapes are decoded are already in operation. Computer devices in such centers do the work of hundreds of clerks. As described by Bell System literature, these machines assemble, translate, sort and summarize all billing information. At the same time new developments in the telephone plant are cutting down on maintenance requirements. A single co-axial cable can carry hundreds of separate telephone conversations, radio programs and television simultaneously with necessary amplification being provided at unattended amplifier stations. Already, co-axial transmission is making way for direct ultra-short wave radio transmission, using unattended tower stations to beam and amplify the signal. The problem of providing dial service to rural communities is being solved in much the same way. Unattended community dial exchanges provide the dial equipment necessary for whole rural areas.

This is but part of the story. Improved testing devices today automatically locate and diagnose trouble and breakdowns. Improved dial systems are becoming more and more troublefree. A simple device permitting subscribers to adjust the loudness of telephone bells without calling the telephone repairman cuts down remarkably on trouble calls.

Speaking to a gathering of business executives not too long ago, Cleo Craig, president of the Bell System parent, American Telephone and Telegraph Company, announced that the Bell System today is 83% mechanized—that is to say, automated. He further announced that within ten years it will be 95% automated, including subscriber toll dialing. Not too long ago Mr. Ben Fairless, at that time president of United States Steel, cited the Bell Telephone System as an enterprise where automation has been accompanied by greater employment. Mr. Fairless spoke too soon. The time now has been reached where telephone industry expansion is being accompanied by an absolute loss in jobs.

In 1954, despite the business recession, the Bell Telephone System had a net gain of 1,400,000 telephones. It would be expected that such large increase would result in increased employment. Actually, however, there was a decrease of 17,500 in Bell System employment.

The story can be told with greater eloquence from available productivity figures. In 1946, there were 51.8 stations per worker and 213 average daily telephone conversations. By 1950, the number of stations per worker had increased to 67.6 and average daily conversations per worker had increased to 269.1. In 1954, telephone stations per worker had increased to 73.7 and conversations were up to 271.5. Automation has been highly profitable to the Bell System. Since 1946, profits per worker have more than doubled, rising from $420 to $961.

What is true of the telephone industry is also true of other major industries. Although steel output rose to 1953 levels this year, this production was achieved with 70,000 fewer workers. In autos, new record production heights have been achieved without any appreciable increase in the labor force. Although U. S. production is at 1953 levels, this has been reached with a million fewer factory workers. Despite alleged prosperity, a hard core of unemployment is persisting and about 3,000,000 are jobless by official figures.

The United Auto Workers estimates that with full automation present production levels in its industry could be reached with about 200,000 workers. This means that four out of five present workers could be displaced permanently from the industry.

There are those who point to the service industries as the answer, declaring that America will need more and more services and that more and more workers will be required for white collar and service jobs. As a union in a service industry, we know that this is not the case, since we already are faced with technological displacement in the office, the operating room and in the plant. Very obviously, America cannot live by having its citizens take in each other's washing and by pressing each other's pants, or for that matter, by selling to each other through small individually owned retail outlets.

It has also been stated that in the long run automation will create more jobs than it will eliminate. Perhaps so. But the long run may be a decade, a century or even a millenium. Meanwhile, any large scale displacement of workers can precipitate a depression of terrifying magnitude. The same condition might also result if new workers are not absorbed into industry.

Dr. Norbet Wiener, Professor of Mathematics at Massachusetts Institute of Technology and father of some of the theory from which automation has been developed, is pessimistic concerning its uses. Pointing out that automation is the equivalent of slave labor, the professor feels that the process may be sadly misused in the rush for quick profits at the expense of labor. Unfortunately, there are indications that Professor Wiener has some real evidence on his side. Only recently M. A. Hollengreen, President of the National Tool Builders Association, declared that automation is a mere matter of semantics, and that such things as a guaranteed annual wage and other safeguards are a mere fear reflex on the part of unions. Such attitudes obviously lend no solutions to the great problems before us.

It is up to us to allay Dr. Wiener's fears. It is up to all men of good will to see that the attitudes of the Mr. Hollengreens of this world shall not determine our future.

There is no doubt that automation can usher in a new and great era, if we begin to act now. Labor must help to find the solutions at the bargaining table in such things as the guaranteed annual wage, negotiated programs for retraining for displaced workers, a shorter work week, longer vacations, better pensions and, above all, higher real wages keeping pace with productivity so that purchasing power might be generated to buy the products of the automated plants.

Collective bargaining is a partial answer. But the problem is of such magnitude that national action is required. We need a national policy on automation which will assure to Americans that this development will bring better living instead of depressions. We need enforcement and strengthening of antitrust laws to insure that automation will not drive out smaller business and lead to super monopolies. We need a good look at the Fair Labor Standards Act, to insure a rising minimum wage with increasing productivity and a shorter legal work week to keep up employment while providing greater leisure to the people. We need free schools for the retaining of workers whose jobs have been eliminated by automation or whose skills have been rendered obsolete.

These are some of the actions that can be undertaken starting now. If we act now to establish the framework for a dynamic economy, insuring reasonable security for our citizens, we can go forward into a truly golden era of prosperity and cultural attainment.


I. W. ABEL, *Secretary-Treasurer, United Steelworkers of America:*

Within a few years recently, the average American has been presented with two products of engineering and the physical sciences. They are the A-Bomb and Automation. People were horrified by the destructive power of the former, but fascinated by the productive power of the latter. Daily, the A-bomb (and the H-bomb) and atomic weapons applications increase in powers of destruction, while those machines, processes, and techniques commonly associated with Automation increase their powers of production.

As research and study continued, people were surprised to find unexpected potentialities in both these fields. Research in the field of atomic energy showed that it could be harnessed for the good of mankind, and progress is being made in that direction. Studies of automation reveal it can create serious problems of social adjustment resulting from its production, but little or nothing is being done to prepare for such an impact. On the contrary, we are confronted with a spectacle of confusion and disagreement among those who are considered "experts" in the field. There is disagreement about the meaning and scope of automation. There is disagreement as to whether this is another genuine industrial revolution, or merely another evolutionary development. There is disagreement as to the probable social dislocation which may result. In the meantime, into this smog of ignorance, confusion and disagreement there appear more and more automative devices.

I prefer to offer suggestions to improve the social effects of automation in the same manner that inventors and manufacturers seek to improve their automative devices. Just as these men are not raising fears while seeking to perfect their products, I do not intend to create anxiety while searching for answers to the social consequences. That is the spirit in which I am raising these points. Since man is not the servant of the machine, but rather the latter should serve man, we must all attempt to determine what will be the probable social problems created by that machine and how to prevent or alleviate them.

There is nothing startling about this, and I can illustrate it with examples from the basic steel industry itself. There have been a great many tremendous technological developments in the steel industry in recent years, but without much public notice. Perhaps the most spectacular of these is the continuous strip mill, which entered upon the scene in the early 1930's. It produces steel sheets among other products. Previously, this flat rolled product called for movement from place to place, being finished on a hand sheet mill. This was hot, laborious work. Now, a thick slab of steel enters a series of rolls, propelled by mechanical power, each set reducing the thickness, increasing the length, and propelling the steel to the next set of rolls, until the steel finally is of the desired guage. Automatically it is then wound like ribbon on a roll. Buttweld tubing is also produced through an application of this continuous flow principle. A spool of flat steel is unwound by mechanical power, the steel then proceeds through a heating furnace traveling slowly enough to be heated to the proper temperature. At the other end of the furnace it is pulled through a funnel-like device which curves the steel ribbon, and the heat of the steel itself welds the edges together into a pipe. There are many applications of this "ribbon on a spool continuous flow" process. There are other examples of automative devices in the basic steel industry.

The strip mill process caused tremendous dislocations. Many old hand mills ceased operations. Thousands of men lost jobs—skilled jobs. Whole communities suffered. No planning had been done. This occurred before the birth of this union.

There is a different atmosphere today. For example, a typical management clause in our basic steel agreements reads in part as follows: "The Company retains the exclusive rights to manage the business and plants and to direct the working forces. The Company, in the exercise of its rights, shall observe the provisions of this Agreement."

Thus, we recognize these rights of management. However management must recognize that it, in turn, has responsibilities. I think that could be a keynote of our approach to the social effects of automation: where there is an insistence upon the free exercise of a right, the voluntary exercise of that right shall be done in a manner not to harm others.

This is not a meaningless statement in our collective bargaining agreements. Under the seniority clause, a worker cannot be displaced or demoted at the whim of the company. Instead, all movements of workers must be made in accordance with the orderly and equitable rules of seniority. If the job on which a worker is retained, or to which he has been moved, has been affected by the exercise of the employer's right, under our wage clause the employee is entitled to an adequate compensation for his new or changed duties. If there is no appropriate job to which he is entitled by right, the company must provide him with some other appropriate job (but not at the expense of another employee entitled to it by seniority) or give the displaced employee compensation in the form of severance pay, in accordance with a scale based upon his seniority and set forth in the agreement itself. This man also has rights under the unemployment compensation laws of his state.

As for all workers who remain employed, they also have the additional rights to have the collective bargaining agreement itself reopened in accordance with the terms of the agreement. The employer receives his benefits from technological change in the form of profits. While there are various criteria used in collective bargaining, profits and productivity are very important ones. Employees should receive their benefits from technological progress in the form of higher wages, shorter hours, vacations, pensions, health and welfare insurance, etc.

We in the Steelworkers Union feel that we have been relatively successful in securing participation in the benefits of technological progress in the steel industry. We intend to continue securing such participation.

Thus this discussion of what has transpired in the basic steel industry might well serve as a pattern for dealing with the broad social effects of Automation. This is as much to the interest of management as it is to the workers affected by automation. After all, a principal reason for production is to sell the product to the consuming public at a reasonable profit. The wages paid workers constitute a large source of the purchasing power of this country. If they had no purchasing power because of the impact of automation, then the very thing that is so efficient and productive has destroyed its own market. After all, only human beings have purchasing power.

We must move rapidly in the attempt to solve the social and economic aspects of automation. Even prior to the uncertainty created by the development in this field, workers in America have increasingly attempted to provide themselves with various forms of security. This is evidenced by the struggle for the guaranteed annual wage, improved pension programs, insurance programs, etc. They have also been vitally concerned with full employment since the unemployed workers do not have a chance to enjoy the foregoing benefits. This is reflected in the growing interest of a shorter work-day or shorter work-week or both. The drive for these types of benefits will be definitely accelerated by the impact of automation.

The road ahead of us is a difficult one. I believe we can meet the social problems of automation. We must!

ADAM ABRUZZI, *Associate Professor of Engineering at the Stevens Institute of Technology:*

A commentator's function is not quite the same as Mark Anthony's. He does not bury by praising; he unearths both by praising and criticizing. It is this Janus-like capacity that I fulfill.

Dr. Campbell remarks that the principal activity of man is to make a living. This statement is as curt as it is true. What is happening is that we are changing how we make a living, and we are changing what we conceive making a living to be.

It seems fashionable and therefore simple to attribute these changes to the new technology. This kind of argument always seems to be advanced whenever problems of human reorganization arise; it is a particular favorite of classical economists who define away fundamental problems by suggesting that they will generate their own solutions in the long run. But to argue that problems solve themselves is to skirt the main issue which is the process of solution.

Human problems are never solved unless some social action is taken. It is social action that solves problems, not problems. New activities and industries will no doubt arise after the new technology is introduced. But technology does not take action; it simply gives signals that action is needed. That action may take many forms and one of them is to create new activities giving new status to people whose old activities have no status.

It is also true but curt to say that mathematical procedures are capable of yielding a theory of the production process. There can never be a full theory of the production process because there can never be a theory which will solve important human problems such as making a living.

We can only have a theory at all because we have broken down many production activities into bits and pieces. Mathematics can never do more than add and multiply bits and pieces, and we cater to this weakness of mathematics by putting things into that form.

The computers that seem as wizard-like as certain mathematical theories are really dullards, too. They have an inexhaustible appetite for adding and multiplying—perhaps even themselves—but they have no appetite for thinking. These machines simply do not think. They are capable of fast rote and uniform rote, but always and only rote. No activities that give man occupational dignity are being given over—mind you, not taken over—to computers or mathematical theories. The new technology is a slave technology in which mechanical workers are slaves capable not of self-emancipation, but of emancipating human workers.

This is to say that there can never be either a mathematical theory or a technology encompassing the distinguished skills of man. There can never be a theory of human worth despite the strenuous efforts of those who seek to define the worth of others, as well as theirs, by adding bits and pieces.

Mechanical slaves are capable of enhancing man's skills and, hence, his stature. But they will not do this of their own accord. They understand only bits and pieces; they know nothing about skill and stature. We, the society, must see to it that the slaves do serve mankind by freeing human workers.

We seem to have made a fashion of embracing the new technology as though we have stumbled on a reputedly wealthy but distant relative. We must welcome him with enthusiasm because he might be bountiful, but we are not quite sure that he won't make off with the silver. We are not convinced that we should ask him in, but we can't seem to find a way to keep him out.

But if we can't keep the new technology out, we can surely ask what it will cost. We can ask not only what it will cost, not only in the impersonal terms of dollars and cents, but also in the personal terms of people.

Dr. Campbell points out that the price of a tight physical system is some instability. The price of a tight social system is also some instability. We must construct social mechanisms to prevent that instability from becoming ruinous, but we can only do this if we are willing to permit temporary instabilities. We may not be able to eliminate temporary instabilities in a physical system; we should not eliminate them in a social system. To borrow again from Dr. Campbell, a society that is great will also be temperamental. It will be temperamental because it permits temporary instabilities. It will be great because it uses to good advantage these signals of how the society is operating.

Now let us take a closer look at some of the more concrete questions. We can start out by observing that the new technology is considered to constitute a revolution of perhaps even greater stature than what is currently called the first industrial revolution. Yet there are still some who would say that the era of automation is really not a revolution because it involves nothing new; they do this perhaps by citing examples of automatic gadgets that were in existence many centuries ago.

It is true that no change is ever so sweeping that some analogy cannot be made to the way things once were. But this is to say that a mountain cannot be steep because there always have been gentle hillocks. If we are willing to see steep mountains, we might see that there was a distinguishable industrial revolution between the first revolution of machines and the new revolution of automation. Like its predecessor this intermediate revolution led to general social and economic changes, though its greatest impact has been on the internal characteristics of industry.

This revolution is the revolution of rationalization, and it began about the turn of this century. It is this revolution, with its insistence on rationalized production methods, rationalized materials handling techniques and rationalized production plans and schedules, that makes the new technology possible. It is mass-production techniques, after all, that give industrial operations the flow characteristics needed for effective automation. Mass-production techniques were made possible, in turn, by the process of breaking down production work into rationalized bits and pieces.

Indeed, the assembly-line, among many others, has all the characteristics of automation except for one thing: it uses human workers instead of mechanical workers. Comparatively little has been made of this man-machine automation, and justifiably so, because, for the most part, human workers perform tasks demanding only slightly more than routine machine skills. Much is made of machine-machine automation, where mechanical workers perform the tasks formerly assigned to human workers, and justifiably so, since the skills of the mechanical workers *are* slightly greater than routine machine skills.

There are many problems with man-machine automation. Some of these will be intensified with machine-machine automation. But none of them will be solved by keeping human workers on tasks that are undistinguished. These tasks are undistinguished precisely because they can be transferred to mechanical workers.

The human worker should and will take on the role of production controller, which is another way of saying that he will exercise distinguished skills. In that role he will judge the worth of production activity, rather than have his own worth judged by production activity. His stature will then be greatly enhanced; he will no longer be competing with mechanical workers for the opportunity of doing undistinguished work whose worth must also be undistinguished.

Worth, of course, is never a clear-cut concept. But the concept of worth does undergo clear-cut changes because occupational codes undergo clear-cut changes. The revolution of rationalization—not without substantial assistance from the earlier revolution of machines—is responsible for the codes that define toil to be godly because things are produced, and that define idleness to be sinful because no things are produced. Indeed, the prevailing code that human worth can be measured in production units is a special case of the toil-idleness doctrine.

We should make sure that occupational codes are oriented in a socially desirable direction if the era of automation is to be fully fruitful. The new codes should recognize that exercising distinguished control skills involves a higher order of accomplishment than exercising undistinguished production skills. The new codes should incorporate the notion that leisure can be dignified, and that it provides an opportunity for expanding skills, not only in a technical sense, but also in the sense of developing a fuller art of living.

To do this, the new codes must provide an opportunity for idleness and even sinfulness. This is the price of all codes that have faith in humanity. Codes that would make distinguished activity possible must also make idleness possible. Codes which hold that idleness must be avoided at all costs must also hold that humanity is not to be trusted. A choice between codes, just as between the technologies from which they always seem to derive, ultimately depends on what the goals of humanity are conceived to be.

While developing these codes we must not forget that we must also solve the problems of transition. These problems require social planning and scheduling. It will not do to say that displaced workers will go into some sort of new activity, and let it go at that. It will not do to consider displaced workers as sacrificial offerings to the hand-washing concept that all will eventually be well.

The problems of transition planning and scheduling are a social cost of the new technology. But there are other social costs as well, and the new technology will surely be less attractive than even the oldest of technologies unless the rewards clearly outbalance the costs.

Engineers recognize the cost problem in designing an automatic factory. They recognize that the swift and economic manufacture of high-quality products by mechanical means cannot be achieved without cost. They recognize that the principal cost is to have adequate information-gathering facilities and adequate control facilities for applying that information.

The same reasoning applies to the non-engineering aspects of automation. The social cost function has the same dimensions of information and control recognized by the engineers. The information here, however, must be gathered by all the components of society, and it must be collated by the general society. Only then is it possible to establish the social controls needed to make sure that automation works in the social sense as well as in an engineering sense.

The thought of social controls is anathema to many people who define social control to be sinful. Paradoxically enough, the same people consider leisure to be sinful. But in neither case can the problems be resolved by inventing labels. The issue is whether the rewards of the new technology are considered socially desirable. If they are, the society must be prepared to pay in terms of social controls.

The question is how to minimize social costs—not to decry the necessity for social controls. The problems are almost terrifying in complexity. But they are not so complex that society must shrink from them. The challenge, like the reward, is not just in the hands of the engineers, but in all our hands.